CW00798097

101 SONGS FOR EASY GUITAR BOOK 8

Wise Publications
part of The Music Sales Group
London/New York/Paris/Sydney/Copenhagen/Berlin/Madrid/Hong Kong/Tokyo

101 SONGS FOR EASY GUITAR BOOK 8

Published by
Wise Publications
14-15 Berners Street, London, W1T 3LJ.

Exclusive distributors:
Music Sales Limited
Distribution Centre, Newmarket Road, Bury St Edmunds,
Suffolk, IP33 3YB, UK.

Music Sales Pty Limited
20 Resolution Drive, Caringbah,
NSW 2229, Australia.

Order No. AM997447
ISBN 978-1-84938-087-4
This book © Copyright 2010 by Wise Publications,
a division of Music Sales Limited.

Unauthorised reproduction of any part
of this publication by any means including
photocopying is an infringement of copyright.

Music arrangements and engraving by Camden Music Limited.
Compiled by Nick Crispin.
Project Editor: Tom Farncombe.

Printed in the EU.

www.musicsales.com

Your Guarantee of Quality:
As publishers, we strive to produce every book
to the highest commercial standards.

The music has been freshly engraved and the book has been
carefully designed to minimise awkward page turns and to make
playing from it a real pleasure. Particular care has been given
to specifying acid-free, neutral-sized paper made from pulps
which have not been elemental chlorine bleached.

This pulp is from farmed sustainable forests and
was produced with special regard for the environment.

Throughout, the printing and binding have been planned
to ensure a sturdy, attractive publication which should give
years of enjoyment.

If your copy fails to meet our high standards, please inform us
and we will gladly replace it.

Ain't No Sunshine
Words & Music by Bill Withers

© Copyright 1971 Interior Music Corporation, USA.
Universal/MCA Music Limited
All rights in Germany administered by Universal/MCA Music Publ. GmbH.
All Rights Reserved. International Copyright Secured.

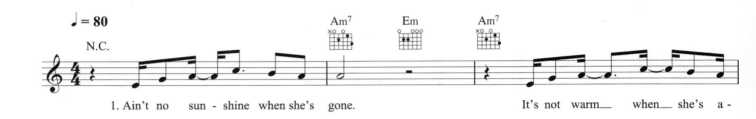

1. Ain't no sun - shine when she's gone. It's not warm___ when___ she's a -

- way. Ain't no sun - shine when she's gone,_____ and she's al - ways gone too

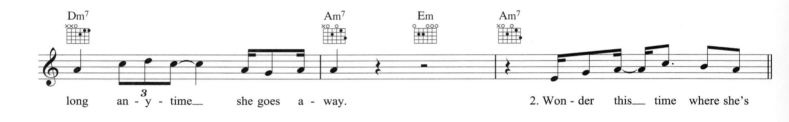

long an - y - time___ she goes a - way. 2. Won - der this___ time where she's

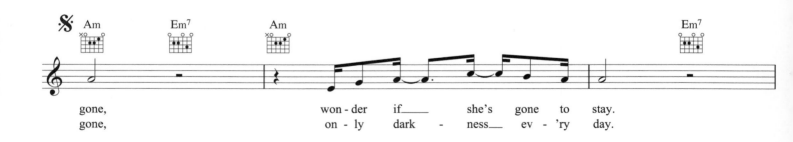

gone, won - der if___ she's gone to stay.
gone, on - ly dark - ness___ ev - 'ry day.

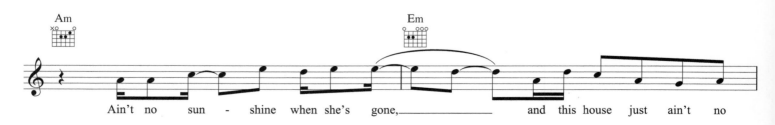

Ain't no sun - shine when she's gone,_____ and this house just ain't no

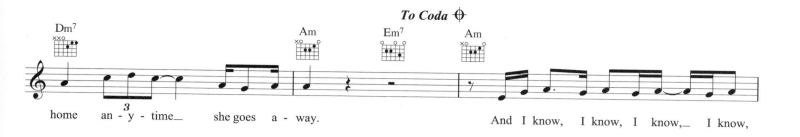

home an-y-time__ she goes a-way. And I know, I know, I know,__ I know,

I know, I know, I know,__ I know,__ I know I know, I know,__ I know,__ I know, I know, I know,

__ I know, I know, I know, I know,__ I know, I know, I know, I know,__ I know, I know, I

know, hey,__ I ought to leave the young thing a-lone,__ but, ain't no sun-shine when she's

gone.__ Ain't no sun-shine when she's

An-y-time__ she goes a-way.

7

Alphabet St.
Words & Music by Prince

© Copyright 1988 Controversy Music, USA.
Universal Music Publishing Limited.
All Rights Reserved. International Copyright Secured.

Adia

Words & Music by
Sarah McLachlan & Pierre Marchand

© Copyright 1997 Sony/ATV Songs LLC/Tyde Music/Studio Nomade Music, Canada.
Sony/ATV Music Publishing (UK) Limited.
All Rights Reserved. International Copyright Secured.

Original key: E♭ (to match original use a Capo, 1st fret)

Ad - i - a, I do___ be - lieve___ I've failed___ you,___

Ad - i - a, I know___ I've let___ you down.___

Don't you know I tried___ so hard___ to love you in___ my way?

It's ea - sy, let it go.___

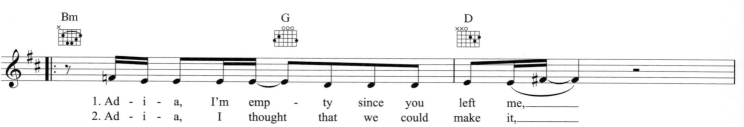

1. Ad - i - a, I'm emp - ty since you left me,___
2. Ad - i - a, I thought that we could make it,___

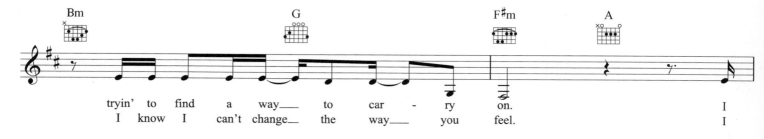

tryin' to find a way___ to car - ry on.
I know I can't change___ the way___ you feel.

I
I

Beautiful Noise
Words & Music by Neil Diamond

© Copyright 1976 Stonebridge Music Incorporated, USA.
Sony/ATV Music Publishing (UK) Limited.
All Rights Reserved. International Copyright Secured.

It's a beau - ti - ful noise,___ made of joy___ and of strife,___

like a sym - phon - y___ played___ by the pass - ing par - ade,___ it's the mu - sic of life.___

It's a beau - ti - ful noise___ and it's a sound that I love,

and it makes me feel good, just like a hand in a glove,___ yes it does,___

___ yes it does.___ What a beau - ti - ful noise

com - in' in - to my room;___ and it's beg - gin' for me

(Synth.)

just to give it a tune.

15

Beggin'
Words & Music by
Bob Gaudio & Peggy Farina

© Copyright 1967 EMI Music Publishing Limited (50%)/EMI Longitude Music (50%).
All Rights Reserved. International Copyright Secured.

Bird On The Wire

Words & Music by Leonard Cohen

© Copyright 1968 Sony/ATV Songs LLC, USA.
Chrysalis Songs Limited.
All Rights Reserved. International Copyright Secured.

horn, I have torn ev-'ry-one___ who reached out for me. But I

swear by this song, and by all___ that I have done wrong, I will make it

all up to thee. I saw a beg-gar lean-ing on his wood-en

crutch. He said to me, "You must not ask for so much."___

And a pret-ty wom-an lean-ing in her dark-ened door, She cried to me,

"Hey, why not ask for more?" More like a bird on the wi-re,___ like a

drunk in a mid-night choir, I have tried in my way to be free.___

Broken Strings

Words & Music by
James Morrison, Nina Woodford & Fraser Thorneycroft-Smith

© Copyright 2008 Chrysalis Music Limited (66.67%)/Sony/ATV Music Publishing (UK) Limited (33.33%).
All Rights Reserved. International Copyright Secured.

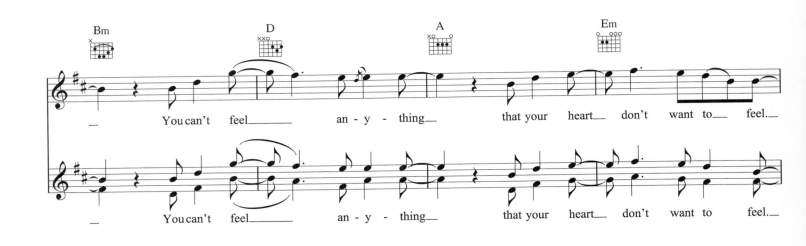

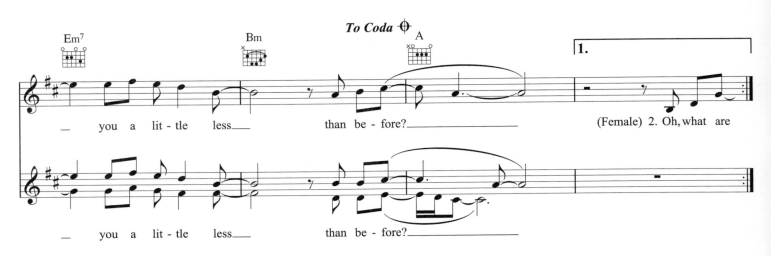

22

Can't Help Falling In Love

Words & Music by
George David Weiss, Hugo Peretti & Luigi Creatore

© Copyright 1961 Gladys Music Incorporated, USA.
Manor Music Company Limited.
All Rights Reserved. International Copyright Secured.

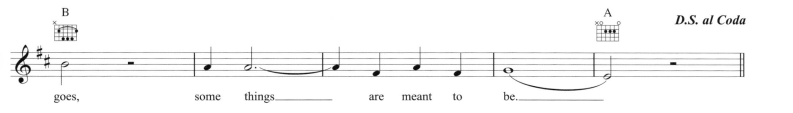

goes,   some things_____ are meant to be._____

⊕ Coda

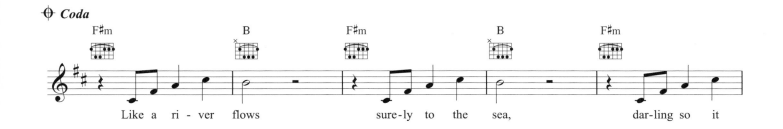

Like a ri - ver flows   sure-ly to the sea,   dar-ling so it

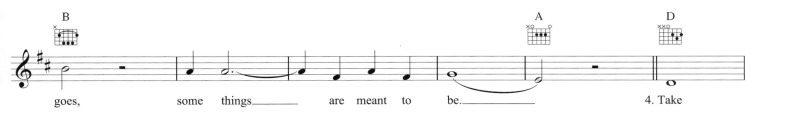

goes,   some things_____ are meant to be._____   4. Take

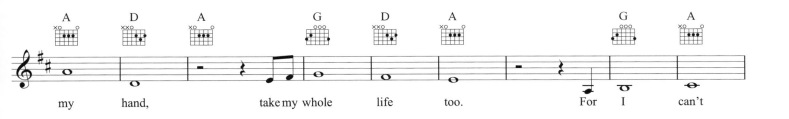

my   hand,   take my whole   life   too.   For I   can't

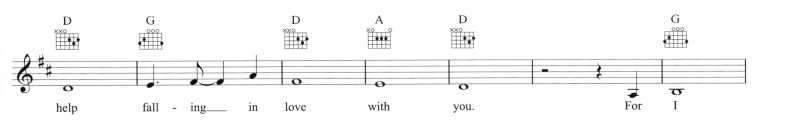

help   fall - ing_____ in love   with   you.   For I

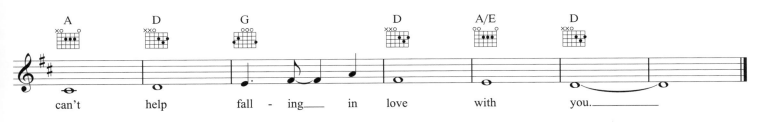

can't   help   fall - ing_____ in love   with   you._____

Call Me The Breeze

Words & Music by J.J. Cale

© Copyright 1971 Johnny Bienstock Music, USA.
Carlin Music Corporation.
All Rights Reserved. International Copyright Secured.

Original key: F# (to match original use a Capo, 2nd fret)

1. They call me the breeze, I keep blow - in' down the road.
(2.) change in the weath - er, ain't no change in me.

They call me the breeze, I keep blow no

Ain't no change in the weath - er,

- in' down the road. I ain't got me no- bod - y,
change in me. I ain't hi - ding from no- bod - y,

I ain't carryin' me no load.
ain't no- bod-y hi - ding from me.

2. Ain't no

3. I got that green light babe, I got to keep mov - in' on.

I got that green light babe, I got to

keep mov - in' on. I might go out to Cal - i - for-

- nia, might go down to Geor - gia, might go home.

Cape Cod Kwassa Kwassa

Words by Ezra Koenig
Music by Ezra Koenig, Rostam Batmanglij,
Christopher Tomson & Christopher Baio

© Copyright 2007 Imagem London Limited.
All Rights Reserved. International Copyright Secured.

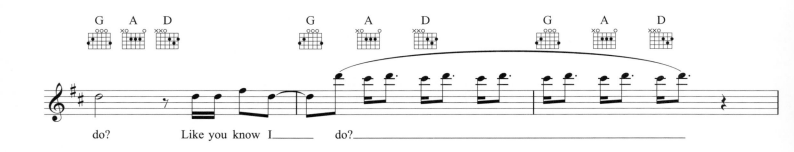

do? Like you know I_____ do?_____

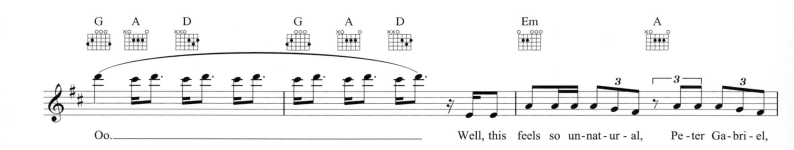

Oo._____ Well, this feels so un-nat-ur-al, Pe-ter Ga-bri-el,

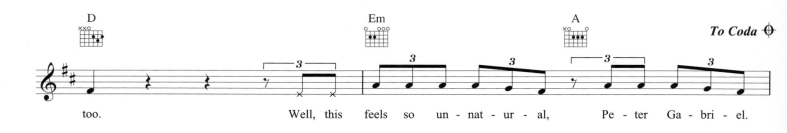

too. Well, this feels so un-nat-ur-al, Pe-ter Ga-bri-el.

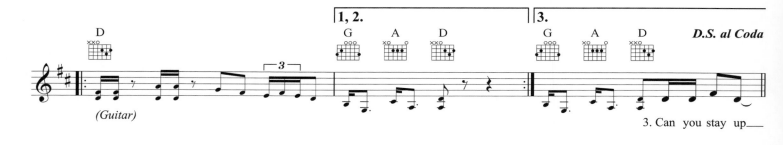

(Guitar) 3. Can you stay up___

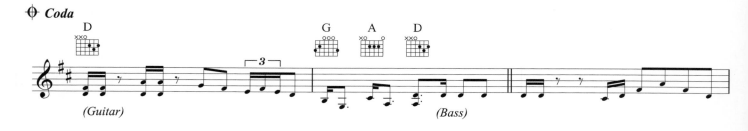

(Guitar) (Bass)

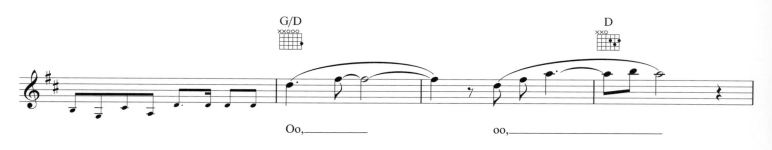

Oo,_____ oo,_____

28

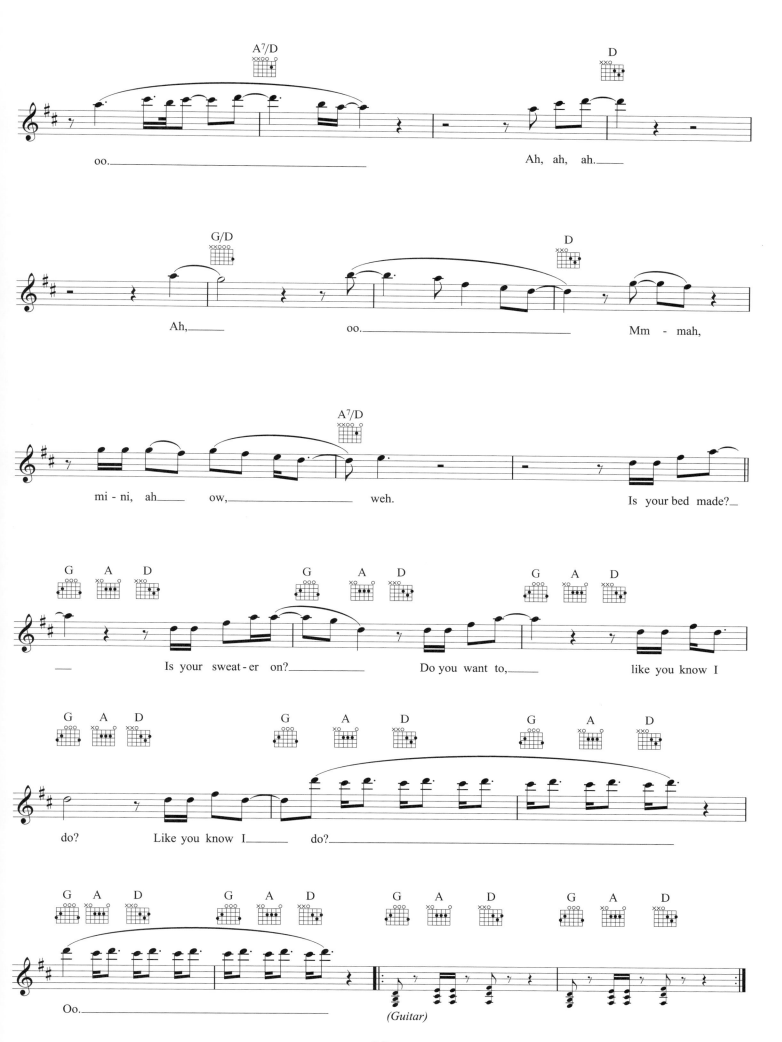

Chasing Cars

**Words & Music by Gary Lightbody, Nathan Connolly,
Jonathan Quinn, Paul Wilson & Tom Simpson**

© Copyright 2006 Universal Music Publishing BL Limited.
All rights in Germany administered by Universal Music Publ. GmbH.
All Rights Reserved. International Copyright Secured.

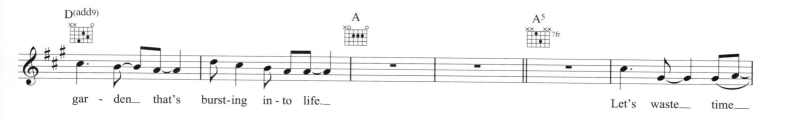

garden that's bursting into life. Let's waste time

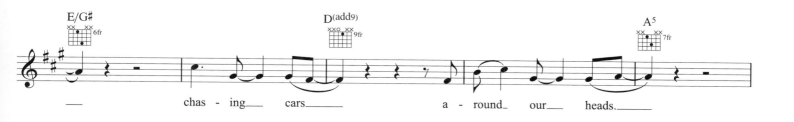

chasing cars around our heads.

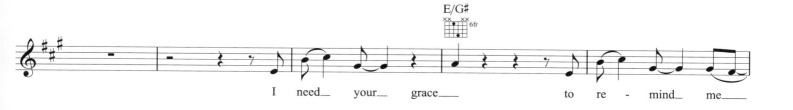

I need your grace to remind me

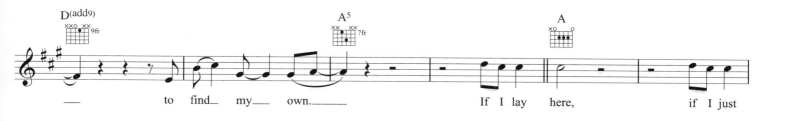

to find my own. If I lay here, if I just

lay here, would you lie with me and just forget the world?

Forget what we're told before we get too old.

Show me a gar - den that's burst-ing in - to life.___ All that I

am, all that I ev - er was___ is here in your per - fect___ eyes,___

they're all I can see.___ I don't know where, con-fused a-bout

how as well,___ just know that these things will nev - er change___ for us at all.___

If I lay here, if I just lay here,___

would you lie with me___ and___ just for - get the world?_

Cuts Like A Knife
Words & Music by
Bryan Adams & Jim Vallance

© Copyright 1982 Adams Communications Incorporated/Testatyme Music/Almo Music Corporation/Irving Music Corporation, USA.
Rondor Music (London) Limited.
All Rights Reserved. International Copyright Secured.

but it feels so right.___ Yeah, cuts like a

knife. Oh,___ but it feels so right.___ 2. There's

times I've been___ mis - ta - ken, there's times I've thought I've been___ mis - und - er - stood.

___ Oo,___ yeah.___ So, wait a min - ute dar - ling,

can't you see___ we did___ the best___ we could?___ Oo,___ we could.___ This

would-n't be the first time___ that things have gone___ as - tray;___ now you've thrown it all___ a - way.___

___ Now, it cuts like a knife, yeah,___ but it feels so

right.___ Oh,___ cuts like a knife.

Chelsea Morning
Words & Music by Joni Mitchell

© Copyright 1969 Crazy Crow Music, USA.
Westminster Music Limited.
All Rights Reserved. International Copyright Secured.

Could You Be Loved
Words & Music by Bob Marley

© Copyright 1980 Fifty-Six Hope Road Music Limited/Odnil Music Limited.
Blue Mountain Music Limited.
All Rights Reserved. International Copyright Secured.

Daydream
Words & Music by John Sebastian

© Copyright 1966 Faithful Virtue Music Company Incorporated, USA.
Windswept Trio Music Company Limited (50%)/Robbins Music Corporation Limited (50%).
All Rights Reserved. International Copyright Secured.

40

(Whistle)

And you can be sure that if you're feel-ing___ right,___ A day-dream will last a-long___

in-to the night.___ To-mor-row at break-fast you may prick up___ your ears,___

Or you may be day-dream-ing for a thou-sand years.___ What a day for a day-

- dream,___ cus-tom made for a day-dream-in' boy.___ And now I'm lost in a day

- dream,___ dream-in' 'bout my bun-dle of joy.___ (Whistle)

Fade to end

41

Dear Mr. Fantasy

Words & Music by
Steve Winwood, Chris Wood & Jim Capaldi

© Copyright 1967 Universal/Island Music Limited (66.67%) (administered in Germany by Universal Music Publ. GmbH)/Warner/Chappell Music Limited (33.33%).
All Rights Reserved. International Copyright Secured.

Dear Mis - ter Fan - tas - y, play us a tune, some - thing to make us all hap - py.

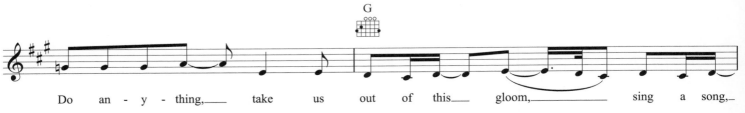

Do an - y - thing, take us out of this gloom, sing a song,

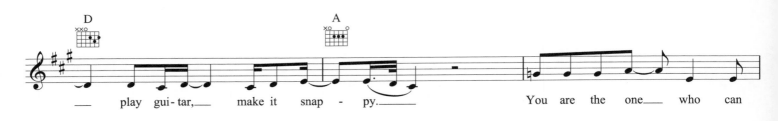

play gui - tar, make it snap - py. You are the one who can

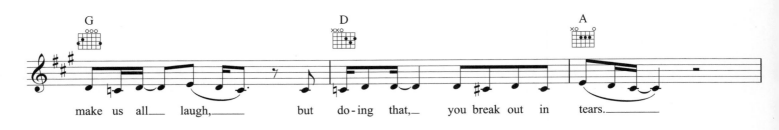

make us all laugh, but do - ing that, you break out in tears.

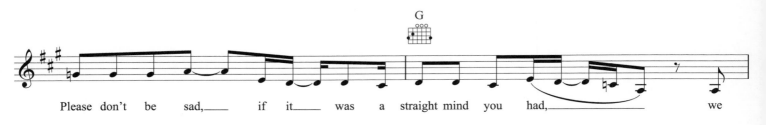

Please don't be sad, if it was a straight mind you had, we

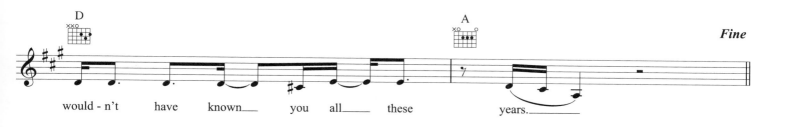

would-n't have known___ you all___ these years.___ *Fine*

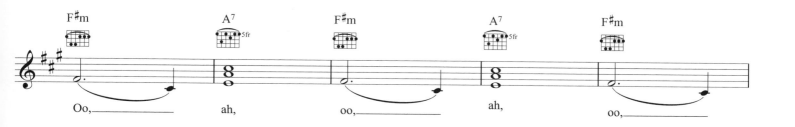

Oo,___ ah, oo,___ ah, oo,___

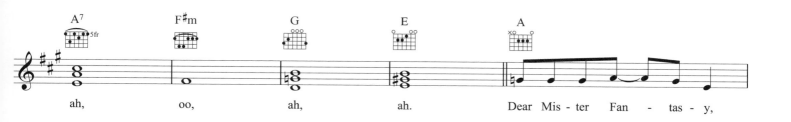

ah, oo, ah, ah. Dear Mis-ter Fan-tas-y,

play us a tune,___ some-thing to make us all___ hap-py.___

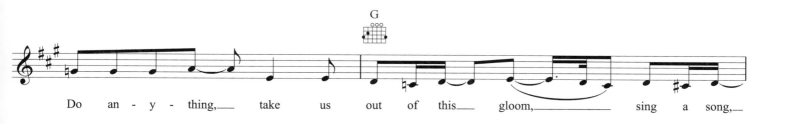

Do an-y-thing,___ take us out of this___ gloom,___ sing a song,___

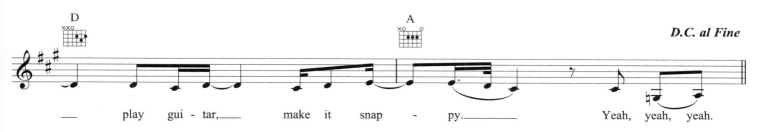

___ play gui-tar,___ make it snap-py.___ Yeah, yeah, yeah. *D.C. al Fine*

Distant Sun
Words & Music by Neil Finn

© Copyright 1993 Roundhead Music/Universal Music Publishing Limited.
All Rights Reserved. International Copyright Secured.

Don't Stop Believin'

Words & Music by
Steve Perry, Neal Schon & Jonathan Cain

© Copyright 1981 Weed High Nightmare Music/Alfred Music Publishing Company Incorporated (75%)/
Lacey Boulevard Music/Sony/ATV Music Publishing (UK) Limited (25%).
All Rights Reserved. International Copyright Secured.

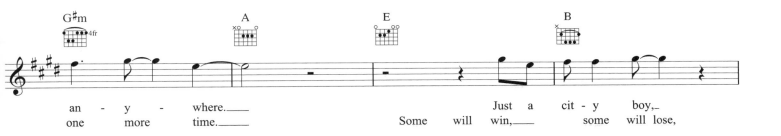

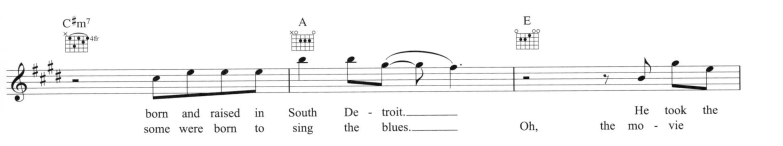

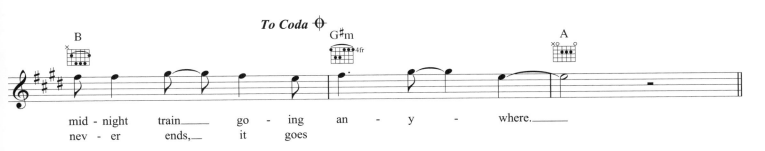

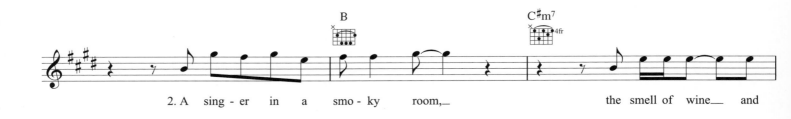

2. A sing - er in a smo - ky room, the smell of wine and

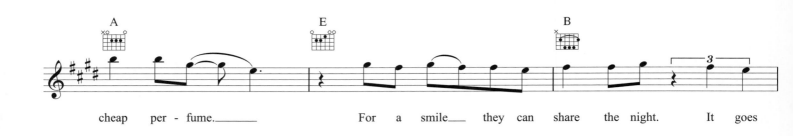

cheap per - fume. For a smile they can share the night. It goes

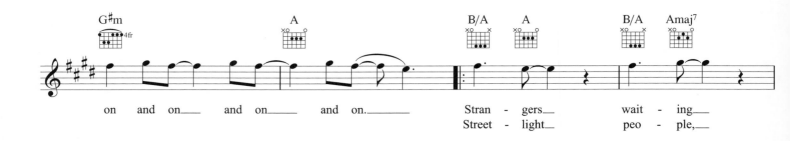

on and on and on and on. Stran - gers wait - ing
Street - light peo - ple,

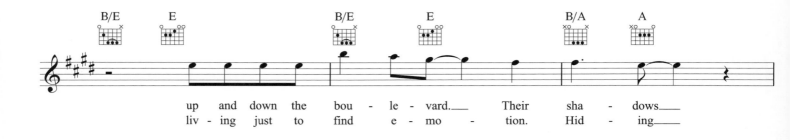

up and down the bou - le - vard. Their sha - dows
liv - ing just to find e - mo - tion. Hid - ing

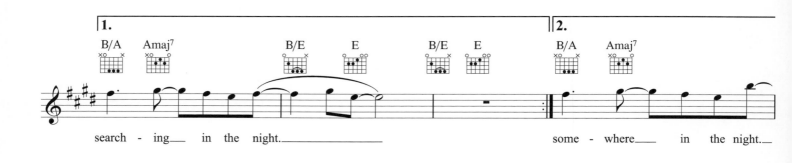

search - ing in the night. some - where in the night.

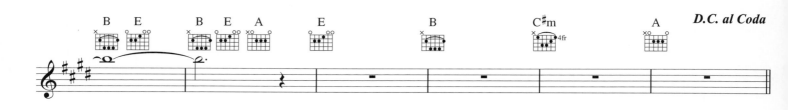

D.C. al Coda

Do It Again

Words & Music by
Donald Fagen & Walter Becker

© Copyright 1972 MCA Music (a division of MCA Incorporated), USA.
Universal/MCA Music Limited.
All rights in Germany administered by Universal/MCA Music Publ. GmbH.
All Rights Reserved. International Copyright Secured.

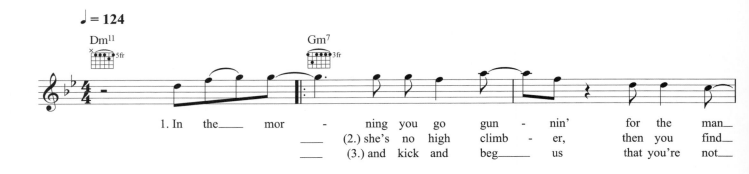

1. In the mor - ning you go gun - nin' for the man
(2.) she's no high climb - er, then you find
(3.) and kick and beg us that you're not

who stole your wa - ter, and you fire till he is done
your on - ly friend. In a room with your two ti -
a gam - blin' man, then you find you're back in Ve -

in, but they catch you at the bor - der. And the mour
- mer, and you're sure you're near the end, then you love
- gas with a han - dle in your hand. Your black cards

- ners are all sing - in' as they drag you by your feet.
a lit - tle wild one and she brings you on - ly sor -
can make you mon - ey, so you hide them when you're a -

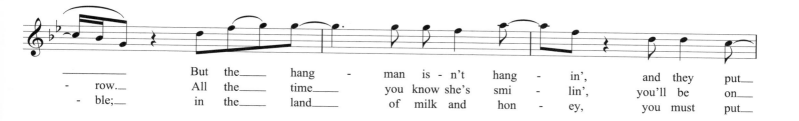

- row.___
But the___ hang - man is - n't hang - in', and they put___

- ble;___
All the___ time___ you know she's smi - lin', you'll be on___

in the___ land___ of milk and hon - ey, you must put___

Cm7   Dm7

___ you___ on the street.___

___ your___ knees to - mor - row.___   You go back,   Jack,

___ them on the ta - ble.___

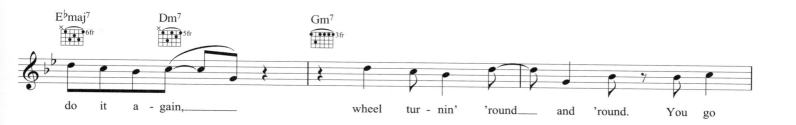

E♭maj7   Dm7   Gm7

do it a - gain,___   wheel tur - nin' 'round___ and 'round.   You go

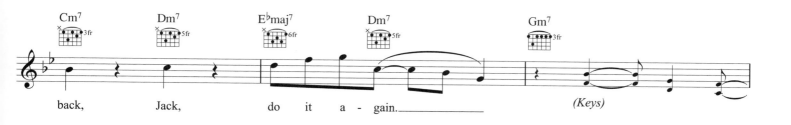

Cm7   Dm7   E♭maj7   Dm7   Gm7

back,   Jack,   do it a - gain.___   *(Keys)*

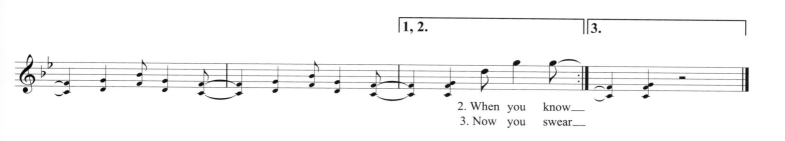

1, 2.   **3.**

2. When you know___

3. Now you swear___

The Dolphins
Words & Music by Fred Neil

© Copyright 1966 Third Story Music Incorporated/19th Opus Publishing, USA.
Carlin Music Corporation.
All Rights Reserved. International Copyright Secured.

And some - times_____ I won - der,_____ do you ev - er_____

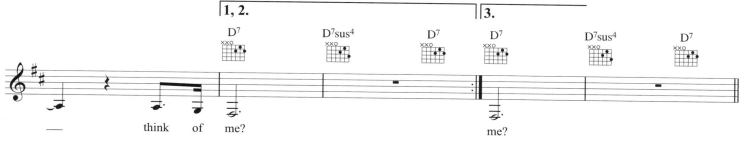

1, 2.   **3.**

_____ think of me?   me?

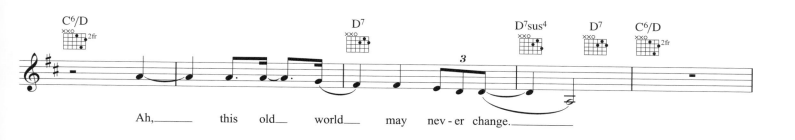

Ah,_____ this old__ world__ may nev - er change._____

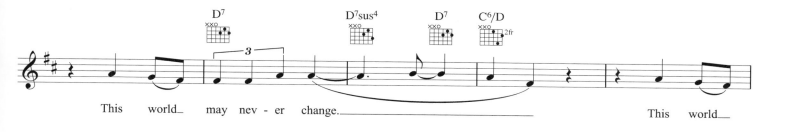

This world__ may nev - er change._____   This world__

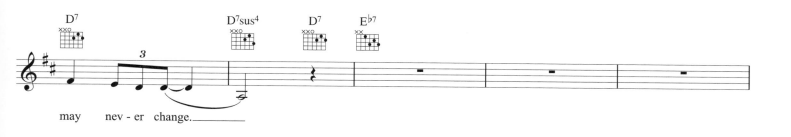

may nev - er change._____

Don't Worry Baby

Words & Music by
Brian Wilson & Roger Christian

© Copyright 1964 Sea Of Tunes Publishing Company/Irving Music Incorporated, USA.
Rondor Music International.
All rights in Germany administered by Rondor Musikverlag GmbH.
All Rights Reserved. International Copyright Secured.

Original key: E (to match original use a Capo, 2nd fret)

1. Well,— it's been build-ing up in-side of me for oh, I— don't know
2. I— guess I should-a kept my mouth shut when I started to brag a-

how— long.— I— don't know why, but I keep think-ing
-bout my— car.— But, I can't back down— now, be-cause I

some-thing's bound— to— go— wrong.— But she looks in my eyes—
pushed the other guys— too far.— She makes me come a-live,—

and makes me re-al-ise,— } and she— says:—
and makes me wan-na drive,— (Don't wor-ry,

Don't— wor-ry, ba — by, ev-'ry-thing— will turn out

ba — by.)— (Don't wor-ry, ba — by.)—

all right. Don't— wor-ry, ba — by,

(Don't wor-ry, ba - by.)— (Don't wor-ry,

55

Downtown Train

Words & Music by Tom Waits

© Copyright 1985 Jalma Music Incorporated, USA.
Universal Music Publishing MGB Limited.
All Rights Reserved. International Copyright Secured.

56

street and past your gate.___ I stand by the light at the four - way.___

You watch them as they fall, oh ba - by, they all have heart at - tacks.

They stay at the car - ni - val, but they'll nev - er win___ you back.

Will I see you to - night on a down - town train,___

where ev - 'ry night, ev - 'ry night it's just the same. Oh ba - by,

will I see you to - night on a down-town train? All of my

dreams just fall like rain,___ oh ba - by, on a down-town train.

Dude (Looks Like A Lady)
Words & Music by Joe Perry, Steven Tyler & Desmond Child

© Copyright 1987 Demon Of Screamin Music/Juju Rhythms/EMI April Music Incorporated/Universal Polygram International, USA.
EMI Songs Limited (49.99%)/Universal Music Publishing Limited (33.34%) (administered in Germany by Universal Music Publ. GmbH)/EMI Music Publishing Limited (16.67%).
All Rights Reserved. International Copyright Secured.

Even Flow

Words by Eddie Vedder
Music by Stone Gossard

© Copyright 1991 Write Treatage Music/Innocent Bystander, USA.
Sony/ATV Music Publishing (UK) Limited (50%)/
Universal Music Publishing Limited (50%) (administered in Germany by Universal Music Publ. GmbH).
All Rights Reserved. International Copyright Secured.

Every Little Thing She Does Is Magic
Words & Music by Sting

© Copyright 1981 Steerpike Limited/Steerpike (Overseas) Limited/EMI Music Publishing Limited.
All Rights Reserved. International Copyright Secured.

1.Though I've tried be-fore to tell her, of the feel-ings I have for her in my heart.

(2.) to tell the sto-ry of a thou-sand rain-y days since we first met?

Ev-'ry-time that I come near her, I just lose my nerve, as I've done from the start.

It's a big e-nough um-brel-la, but it's al-ways me that ends up get-ting wet.

Ev-'ry lit-tle thing she does is ma-gic, ev-'ry-thing she do just turns me on.

Ev-en though my life be-fore was tra-gic, now I know my love for her goes on.

To Coda

2.Do I have

65

Everywhere
Words & Music by Christine McVie

© Copyright 1987 Fleetwood Mac Music, USA.
Universal Music Publishing MGB Limited.
All rights in Germany administered by Musik Edition Discoton GmbH.
All Rights Reserved. International Copyright Secured.

1. Can you hear me call-ing out your name?_ You know that I've fall - en in and I don't know what to say._ I'll speak a lit - tle loud - er, I'll e - ven shout._ You know that I'm proud and I can't get the words out. Oh, I,_____ I wan-na be with you ev - 'ry-where._ (Oh) (Guitar) 2. Some - thing's happ 'ning, hap-pen-ing to me._ My friends say___ I'm act - ing pe - cu - liar - ly._ C'mon ba - by, we bet - ter make a start._ You bet - ter make it soon be-fore you break my heart._ Oh,

Expecting To Fly
Words & Music by Neil Young

© Copyright 1967 Ten East Music, USA.
Universal Music Publishing MGB Limited.
All Rights Reserved. International Copyright Secured.

There you stood on the edge of your feath-er, ex-pect-ing to fly.

While I laughed, I won-dered wheth-er

I could wave good-bye, know-ing that you'd gone

By the sum-mer it was heal-ing,

we had said good-bye. All the years we'd spent with feel-ing

end-ed with a cry, babe, end-ed with a cry,

Flowers On The Wall

Words & Music by Lewis C. DeWitt

© Copyright 1965 (Renewed) Unichappell Music Incorporated, USA.
Carlin Music Corporation.
All Rights Reserved. International Copyright Secured.

Original key: B (to match original use a Capo, 2nd fret)

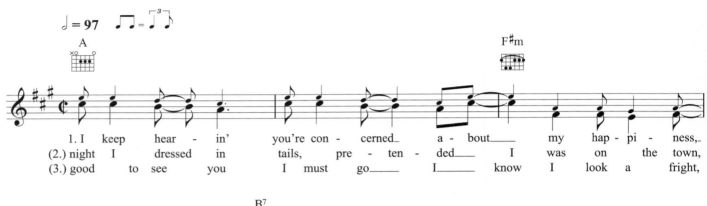

1. I keep hearin' you're concerned about my happiness,
(2.) night I dressed in tails, pretended I was on the town,
(3.) good to see you I must go I know I look a fright,

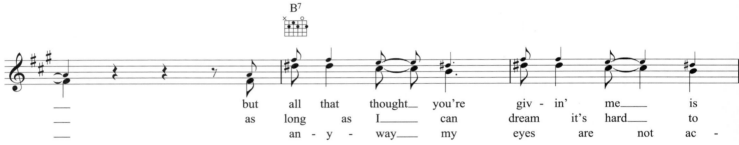

but all that thought you're givin' me is
as long as I can dream it's hard to
anyway my eyes are not ac-

con-science I guess. If I were walkin'
slow this swinger down. So please don't give a
-customed to this light. And my shoes are

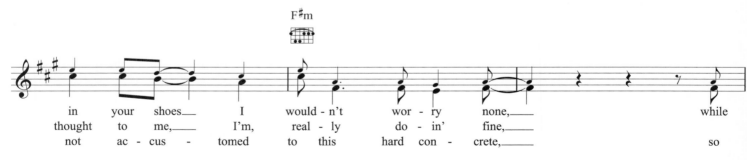

in your shoes I wouldn't worry none, while
thought to me, I'm, really doin' fine,
not accustomed to this hard concrete, so

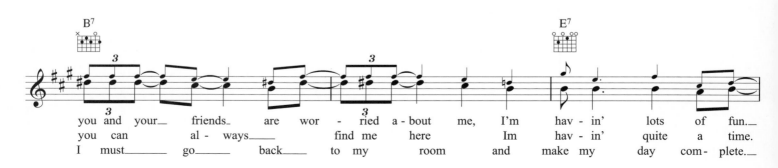

you and your friends are worried about me, I'm havin' lots of fun.
you can always find me here Im havin' quite a time.
I must go back to my room and make my day complete.

72

Count - in' flow - ers on the wall,_____ that don't

both - er me at all._____ Play - in'

sol - it - aire_____ till dawn with a deck_____ of fif - ty -

one. Smok - in' cig - ar - ettes_____ and

watch - in' Cap - tain Kan - gar - oo_____ now don't_ tell_

me, I've noth - ing to do!_____ 2. Last
3. It's

do!_____ Don't tell me,

I've noth - ing to do!_____

73

Games People Play
Words & Music by Joe South

© Copyright 1968 Sony/ATV Music Publishing (UK) Limited.
All Rights Reserved. International Copyright Secured.

Get Rhythm
Words & Music by John R. Cash

© Copyright 1956 Hi-Lo Music Incorporated/Unichappell Music Incorporated, USA.
Carlin Music Corporation.
All Rights Reserved. International Copyright Secured.

shined my shoe__ how'd he keep__ from get-ting the blues?_ He grinned as he raised his

sweat a - way, I said you mighty lit-tle boy to be a - work-ing that way._ He said I like it with a

lit - tle head,__ he popped his shoe - shine rag and then he__ said, get rhy - thm

big wide grin__ kept on a-pop - ping and he say it again get rhy - thm

B♭

when you get the blues,__ come on__ get rhy-thm when

when you get the blues,__ come on__ get rhy-thm when

F

you get the blues,__ a jump-ing rhy - thm makes you feel so fine__ it-'ll

you get the blues,__ it only cost a dime just a nickle a shoe it does a

B♭

shake all your trou - ble from your wor - ried mind,__ get rhy - thm

mil - lion dol - lars worth of good for you,__ get rhy - thm

1. **C** **F**

when you get the blues.__

when you get the blues.__

Get

2. **C** **F**

when you get the blues.__

77

Gimme All Your Lovin'

Words & Music by
Billy Gibbons, Dusty Hill & Frank Beard

© Copyright 1983 Stage Three Songs Incorporated, USA.
Administered in the UK & Eire by Stage Three Music Limited.
All Rights Reserved. International Copyright Secured.

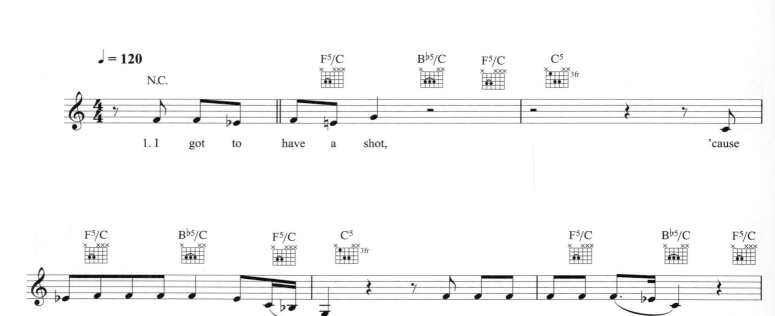

1. I got to have a shot, 'cause

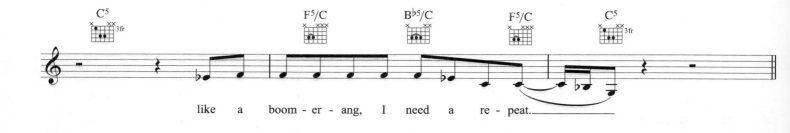

what you got is oh, so sweet._____ You got to make it hot,_____

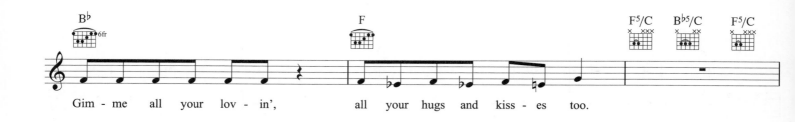

like a boom-er-ang, I need a re-peat._____

Gim-me all your lov-in', all your hugs and kiss-es too.

Gim-me all your lov-in', don't let up un-til we're through._____

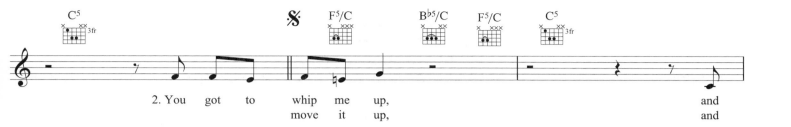

2. You got to whip me up, and
   move it up, and

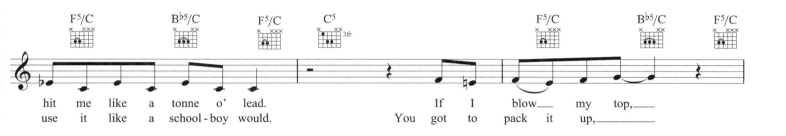

hit me like a tonne o' lead. If I blow my top,
use it like a school-boy would. You got to pack it up,

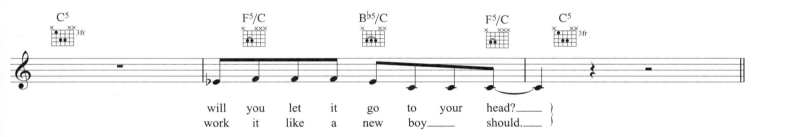

will you let it go to your head?
work it like a new boy should.

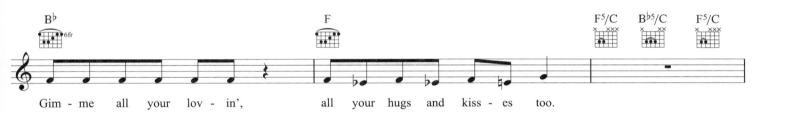

Gim-me all your lov-in', all your hugs and kiss-es too.

Gim-me all your lov-in', don't let up un-til we're through.

(Guitar)

3. You got to

Grace

Words & Music by
Jeff Buckley & Gary Lucas

© Copyright 1994 Sony/ATV Tunes LLC/El Viejito Music/Gary Lucas Music, USA.
Sony/ATV Music Publishing (UK) Limited (50%)/Universal/MCA Music Limited (50%) (administered in Germany by Universal/MCA Music Publ. GmbH).
All Rights Reserved. International Copyright Secured.

1. There's the moon ask-ing to stay long e-nough for the clouds to fly me a-way.
2. And she weeps on my arm, walk-ing to the bright lights in sor-row.
3. And I feel them drown my name, so ea-sy to know and forget with this kiss.

Oh, it's my time com-ing, I'm not a-fraid, (a-)fraid to die. My
Oh, drink a bit of wine, we both might go to-mor-row, oh, my love. And the
I'm not a-fraid to go, but it goes so slow...

fad-ing voice sings of love.
rain is fall-ing and I be-lieve my time has come.

But she cries to the click-ing of time, oh, time.
It re-minds me of the pain I might leave, leave be-hind.

80

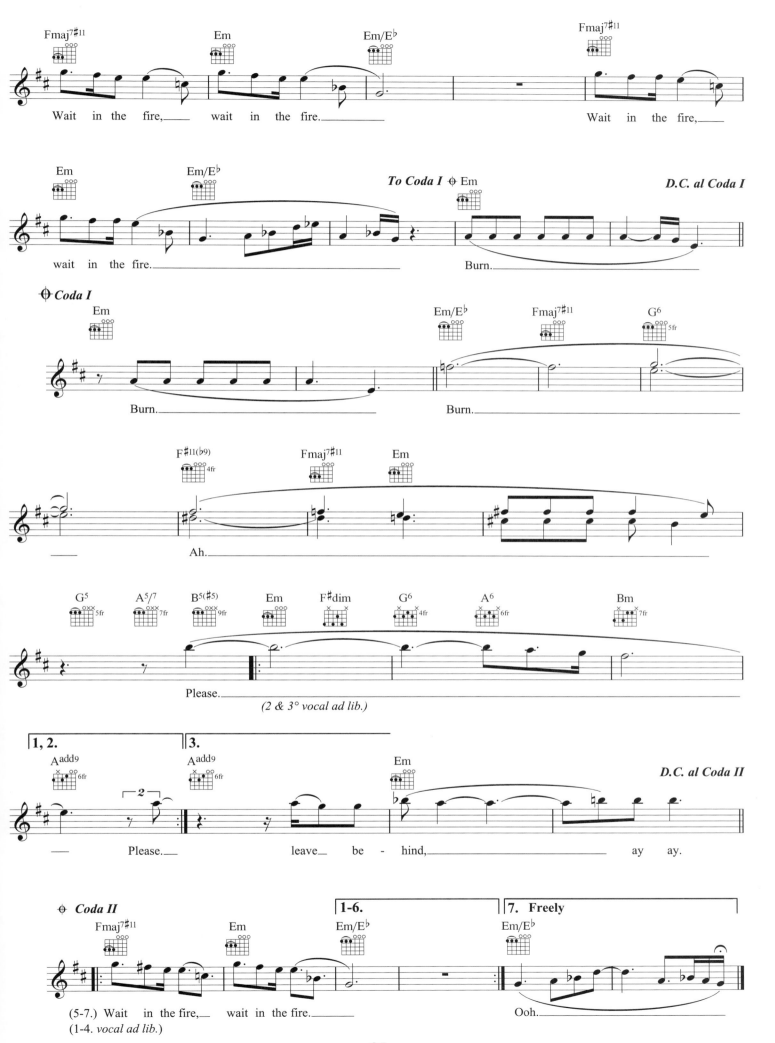

Here Comes The Night
Words & Music by Bert Russell

© Copyright 1964 Bert Russell Music LLC, USA.
The International Music Network Limited.
All Rights Reserved. International Copyright Secured.

Whoa, here it____ comes.____

Here comes the night,_____ here comes the night._____

Whoa,_____ yeah.____

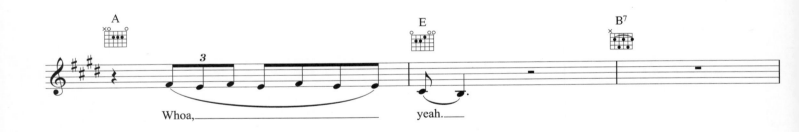

1. I could see right out my win - dow, walk - in' down the street, my girl____ with an -
2. There they go, it's funny how they look so good to - geth - er, won - der what is
3. She's with him, he's turning down the lights and now he's hold - ing her the way I

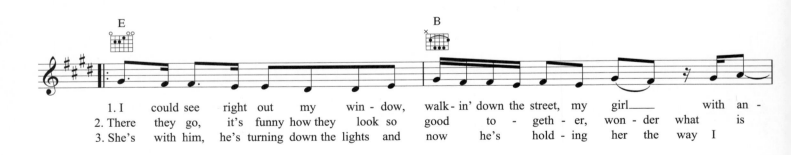

- oth - er guy.____
wrong with me?____
used to do.____

His arms a - round her like it used to be with
Why can't I ac - cept the fact she's
I could see her clos - ing her eyes and

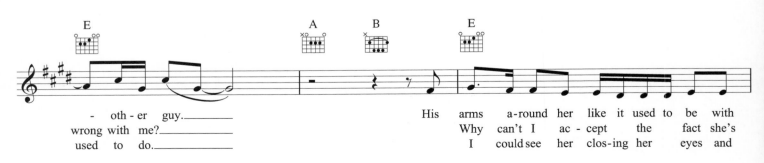

Hey, Good Lookin'

Words & Music by Hank Williams

© Copyright 1951 Sony/ATV Acuff Rose Music, USA.
Sony/ATV Music Publishing (UK) Limited.
All Rights Reserved. International Copyright Secured.

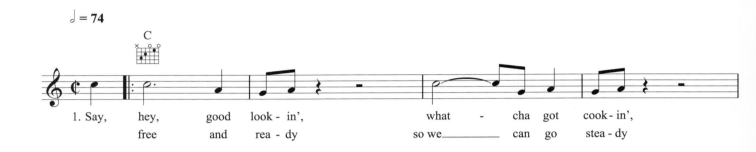

1. Say, hey, good look - in', what - cha got cook - in',
free and rea - dy so we can go stea - dy

how's a - bout cook - in' some - thin' up with me.
how's a - bout sav - in' all your time for me?

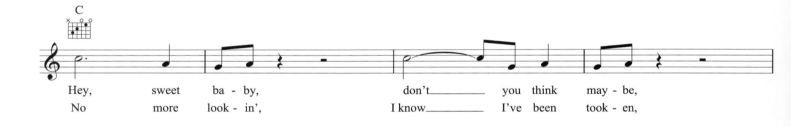

Hey, sweet ba - by, don't you think may - be,
No more look - in', I know I've been took - en,

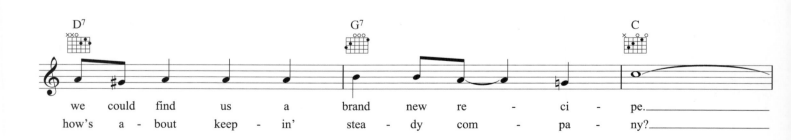

we could find us a brand new re - ci - pe.
how's a - bout keep - in' stea - dy com - pa - ny?

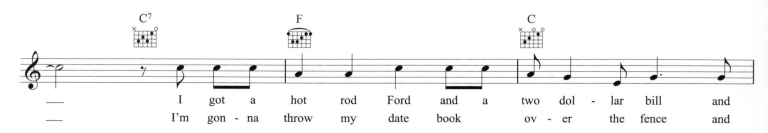

— I got a hot rod Ford and a two dol - lar bill and
— I'm gon - na throw my date book ov - er the fence and

I know a spot right ov-er the hill.___ There's so-da pop and the
find me one for five or ten cents.___ I'll keep it 'til it's

danc-in's free.___ So if you wan-na have fun come a-long with me.___
cov-ered with age___ 'cause I'm writ-in' your name on ev-er-y page.___

Hey, good look-in', what - - cha got

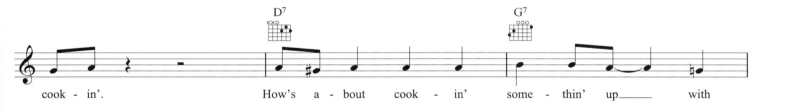

cook-in'. How's a-bout cook-in' some-thin' up___ with

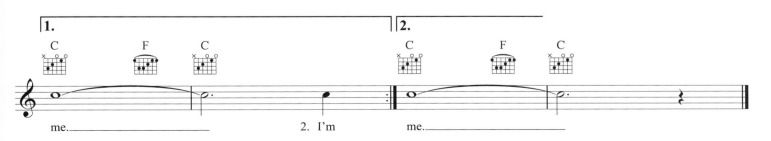

me.___   2. I'm   me.___

85

Hi Ho Silver Lining

Words & Music by
Scott English & Laurence Weiss

© Copyright 1967 Helios Music Company/Claus Ogermann Production und Musikverlag oHG, Germany.
All Rights Reserved. International Copyright Secured.

1. You're ev-'ry-where and no-where, ba - by. That's where you're at.
2. Flies are in your pea soup, ba - by. They're wav-ing at me.

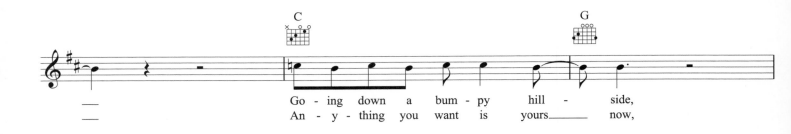

Go - ing down a bum - py hill - side,
An - y - thing you want is yours___ now,

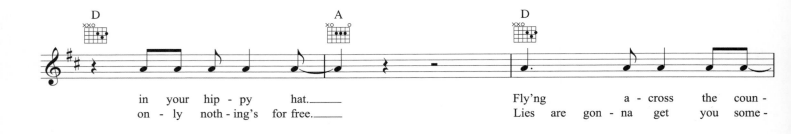

in your hip - py hat.___ Fly'ng a - cross the coun -
on - ly noth - ing's for free.___ Lies are gon - na get you some -

- try and get - ting fat,___ say - ing ev - 'ry - thing is groov -
- day, just wait and see.___ o - pen up your beach um - brel -

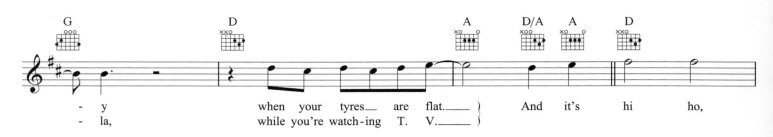

- y when your tyres are flat.___) And it's hi ho,
- la, while you're watch - ing T. V.___)

sil - ver lin - ing, an - y - where you go. Now, ba - by, I see your

sun is shin - ing, but I won't make a fuss, though it's

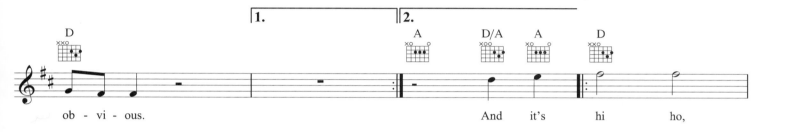

ob - vi - ous. And it's hi ho,

sil - ver lin - ing, an - y - where you go. Well, ba - by,

I see your sun is shin - ing, but I won't make a fuss,

Repeat and fade

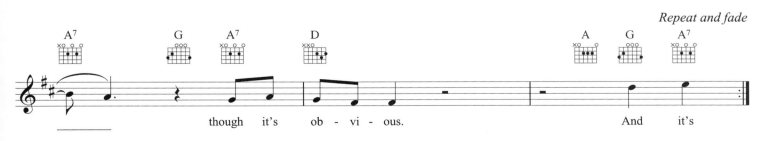

though it's ob - vi - ous. And it's

Holidays In The Sun

Words & Music by
Johnny Rotten, Steve Jones, Paul Cook & Sid Vicious

© Copyright 1977 Universal Music Publishing Limited (75%) (administered in Germany by Universal Music Publ. GmbH)/
Warner/Chappell Music Limited (25%).
All Rights Reserved. International Copyright Secured.

They're sta-ring all night and they're sta-ring all day. I____ had no rea-son to be

here at all,____ and now I've got a rea-son, it's no real rea-son and I'm wait-ing,____

the Ber-lin Wall.

(spoken) I got to go over the Berlin wall. I don't understand this thing at all.
I'm gonna go over the Berlin wall, I'm gonna go over the Berlin wall,
I'm gonna go over the Berlin wall!

Clau-stro-pho-bi-a, there's too much pa-ra-noi-a, there's too ma-ny clo-sets, so

when will we fall? And now I've got a rea-son, it's no real rea-son to be wai-ting,____ the Ber-lin

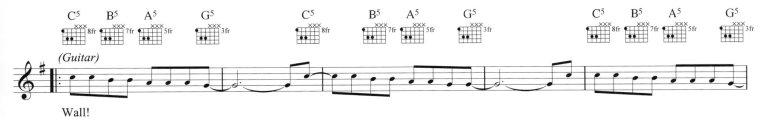

(Guitar)

Wall!

(spoken) I got to go over the wall, I don't understand this thing at all. This third rate B-movie show. Cheap dialogue, cheap essential scenery.
I got to go over the wall. I wanna go over the Berlin wall, before they come over the Berlin wall. I don't understand this thing at all,
I'm gonna go over the wall. I wanna go over the Berlin wall, I'm gonna go over the Berlin wall, before they come over the Berlin wall!

(spoken) I don't understand this thing at all.
Please don't be waiting for me!

Homeward Bound

Words & Music by Paul Simon

© Copyright 1966 Paul Simon Music, USA.
All Rights Reserved. International Copyright Secured.

Home - ward___ bound,   I wish I was,_____ home - ward___

bound.   Home,   where my thought's___ es - ca - ping,

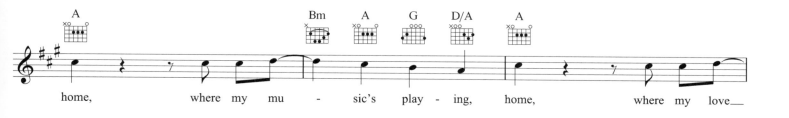

home,   where my mu - sic's play - ing, home,   where my love___

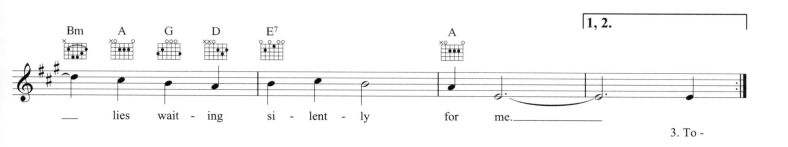

1, 2.

___ lies wait - ing si - lent - ly for me.___

3. To -

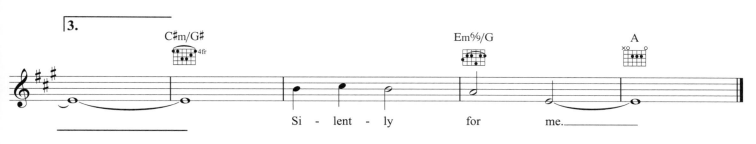

3.

Si - lent - ly for me.___

91

Here Comes Your Man
Words & Music by Charles Thompson

© Copyright 1989 Rice And Beans Music, USA.
Universal/MCA Music Limited
All rights in Germany administered by Universal/MCA Music Publ. GmbH.
All Rights Reserved. International Copyright Secured.

1. Out - side there's a box - car wait - ing, out - side the fam - 'ly stew.

Out by the fire breath - ing. Out - side, we wait 'til face turns blue.

I know the ner - vous walk - ing, I know the dirt - y beard hangs.

Out by the box - car wait - ing, take me a - way to

no - where plains. There is a wait, so long. You nev - er wait so

long. Here comes your man, here comes your

man, here comes your man.

ooh.

There is a wait, so long. You nev-er wait so

long. Here comes your man,

here comes your man, here comes your man,

1.
here comes your man. 2. here comes your man.

Here comes your man, here comes your man, here comes your

man, here comes your man, here comes your man.

Human

Words by Brandon Flowers
Music by Brandon Flowers, Dave Keuning, Mark Stoermer & Ronnie Vannucci

© Copyright 2008 Universal Music Publishing Limited.
All rights in Germany administered by Universal Music Publ. GmbH.
All Rights Reserved. International Copyright Secured.

1. I did my best to no - tice when the call came down the line.__
(2.)- spects to grace and vir - tue, send my con - do - len - ces to good.

__ Up to the plat - form of sur - ren - der I was brought but I was kind.__
__ Give my re - gards to soul and ro - mance, they al - ways did the best they could.__

__ And some - times I get ner - vous when I see an o - pen door.__
__ And so long to de - vo - tion, you taught me ev -'ry - thing__ I know.__

__ Close your eyes,__ clear your heart,__
__ Wave good - bye,__ wish me well.__

cut the cord.__ Are we hu - man or are we dan -
You've got - ta let me go.__

- cer? My sign is vi - tal, my hands are cold.__

I Guess That's Why They Call It The Blues

Words & Music by Elton John, Bernie Taupin & Davey Johnstone

© Copyright 1983 HST Management Limited/Rouge Booze Incorporated/Big Pig Music Limited.
Universal Music Publishing Limited.
All rights in Germany administered by Universal Music Publ. GmbH.
All Rights Reserved. International Copyright Secured.

I Have A Dream

Words & Music by
Benny Andersson & Björn Ulvaeus

© Copyright 1979 Union Songs AB, Sweden.
Bocu Music Limited for Great Britain and the Republic of Ireland.
All rights in Germany administered by Universal Music Publ. GmbH.
All Rights Reserved. International Copyright Secured.

I'm Sticking With You
Words & Music by Lou Reed

© Copyright 1985 Garnant Music, USA.
Universal/Island Music Limited.
All Rights Reserved. International Copyright Secured.

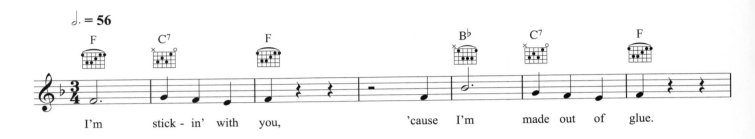

I'm stick - in' with you, 'cause I'm made out of glue.

To Coda ⊕

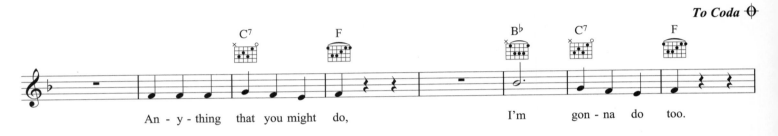

An - y - thing that you might do, I'm gon - na do too.

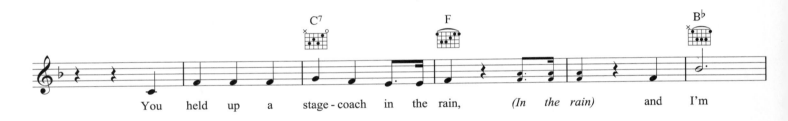

You held up a stage - coach in the rain, *(In the rain)* and I'm

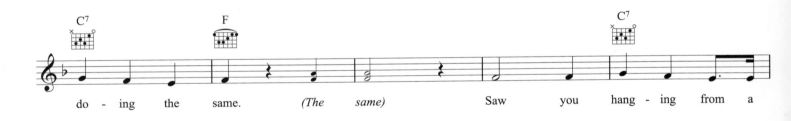

do - ing the same. *(The same)* Saw you hang - ing from a

D.C. al Coda

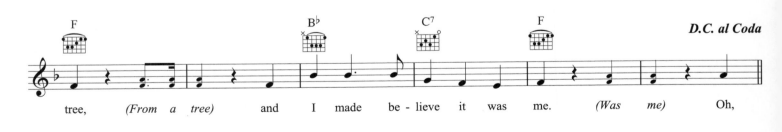

tree, *(From a tree)* and I made be - lieve it was me. *(Was me)* Oh,

⊕ *Coda*

Ma - ny peo - ple go - ing to the strat - o - sphere.

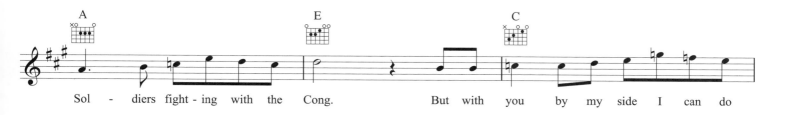

Sol - diers fight-ing with the Cong. But with you by my side I can do

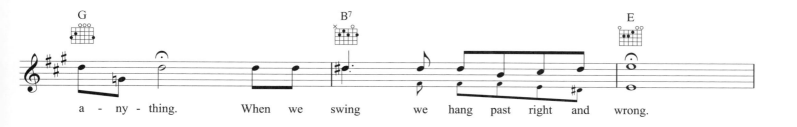

a - ny - thing. When we swing we hang past right and wrong.

♩ = 82
(A tempo)

(N.C.)

I'll do an - y - thing for you, ba - by, an - y-

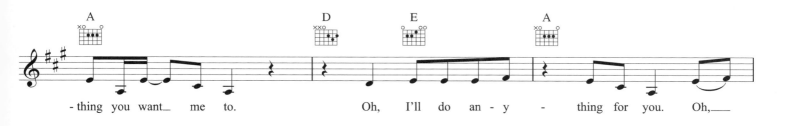

- thing you want__ me to. Oh, I'll do an - y - thing for you. Oh,___

play 8 times

oh, I'm stick - in' with you. Oh,___ oh, I'm stick - in' with

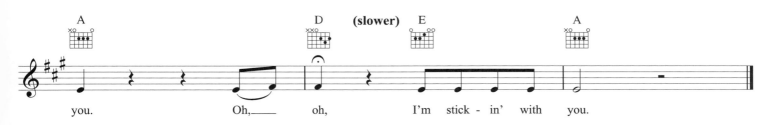

(slower)

you. Oh,___ oh, I'm stick - in' with you.

I Can't Dance

Words & Music by
Phil Collins, Tony Banks & Mike Rutherford

© Copyright 1991 Imagem Music.
All Rights Reserved. International Copyright Secured.

Jive Talkin'

Words & Music by
Barry Gibb, Maurice Gibb & Robin Gibb

© Copyright 1975 Gibb Brothers Music (66.66%)/Warner/Chappell Music Limited (33.34%).
All Rights Reserved. International Copyright Secured.

Lay Lady Lay

Words & Music by Bob Dylan

© Copyright 1969 (Renewed 1997) Big Sky Music, USA.
All Rights Reserved. International Copyright Secured.

Like A Prayer

Words & Music by
Madonna & Pat Leonard

© Copyright 1989 Webo Girl Publishing Incorporated/Bleu Disque Music Company Incorporated/Johnny Yuma Music/Orangejello Music, USA.
Warner/Chappell Music Publishing Limited (50%)/EMI Music Publishing Limited (25%)/Sony/ATV Music Publishing (UK) Limited (25%).
All Rights Reserved. International Copyright Secured.

Life is a mys - ter - y, ev - 'ry - one must stand a - lone.

I hear you call my name, and it feels like home.

When you call my name, it's like a lit - tle prayer,

I'm down on my knees, I wan - na take you there. In the mid - night hour,

I can feel your power, just like a prayer, you know I'll take you

there. 1. I hear your voice, it's like an an -
2. Like a child, you whis - per

- gel sigh - ing.   I have no choice, I hear your
soft - ly to me.   You're in con - trol, just like a

113

Linger

Words by Dolores O'Riordan
Music by Dolores O'Riordan & Noel Hogan

© Copyright 1992 Island Music Limited.
Universal/Island Music Limited.
All rights in Germany administered by Universal Music Publ. GmbH.
All Rights Reserved. International Copyright Secured.

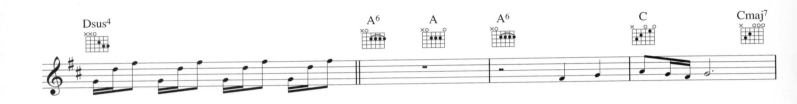

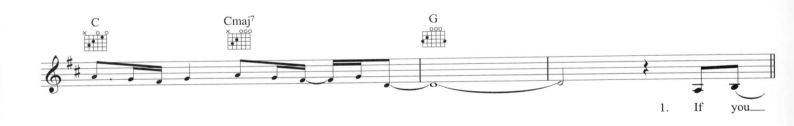

1. If you

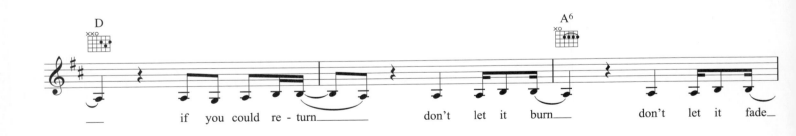

if you could re-turn don't let it burn don't let it fade

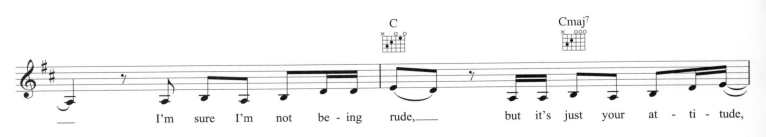

I'm sure I'm not be-ing rude, but it's just your at-ti-tude,

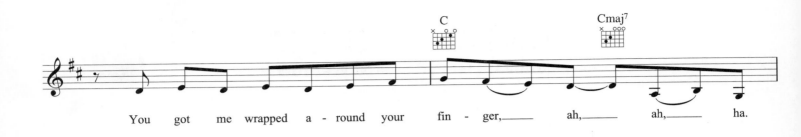

You got me wrapped a-round your fin - ger,___ ah,___ ah,___ ha.

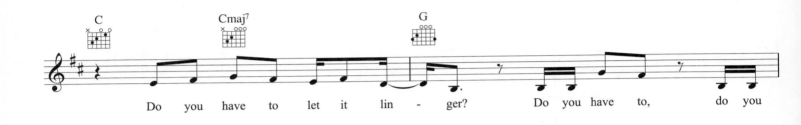

Do you have to let it lin - ger? Do you have to, do you

1.

have to, do you have to let it lin - ger?___

Oh I thought the world__ of you,___ I thought no-thing could__ go wrong,

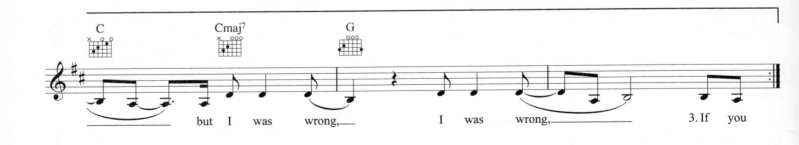

but I was wrong,___ I was wrong,___ 3. If you

2.

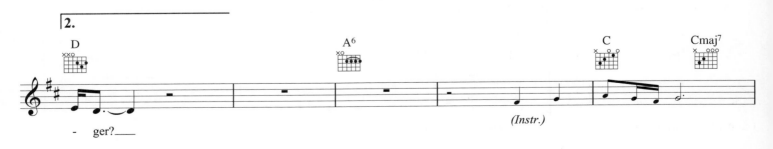

- ger?___ *(Instr.)*

D.S. al Coda

And I'm in _____ so

Coda

- ger? _____ You know I'm such a fool _____ for you
- ger? _____ *(2° vocal tacet)*

you got me wrapped a - round your fin - ger, ___ ah, ___ ah, ___ ha. Do you have to let it lin -

- ger? Do you have to, do you have to, do you have to let it lin -

Play 3 times

Let Your Love Flow

Words & Music by Larry E. Williams

© Copyright 1976 Figs D Music Incorporated, USA.
Minder Music Limited.
All Rights Reserved. International Copyright Secured.

Original Key: E♭ (to match original use a Capo, 1st fret)

♩ = 112

1. There's a rea - son for the sun - shine_ sky_ and there's a
(2.) rea - son for the warm sweet_ nights_ there's a

rea - son why I'm feel - ing so high,_ must be the sea - son when that
rea - son for the can - dle_ lights, must be the sea - son when those

love light shines_ all a - round us. So let that feel - ing grab you
love rites shine_ all a - round us. So let the won - der take you

deep in - side_ and send you reel - ing where your love can't hide_ and then go
in - to_ space_ and lay you un - der it's lov - ing em - brace_ just feel the

steal - ing through the moon - lit nights_ with your lov - er.
thun - der as it warms your face_ you can't hold_ back.

Just let your

120

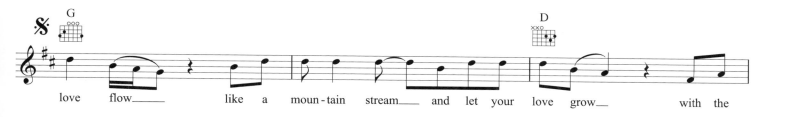

love flow_____ like a moun-tain stream____ and let your love grow_____ with the

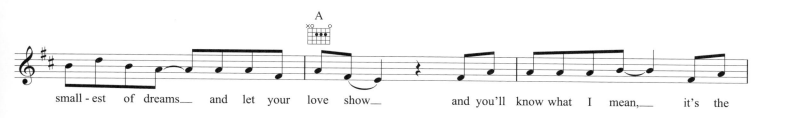

small-est of dreams____ and let your love show____ and you'll know what I mean,____ it's the

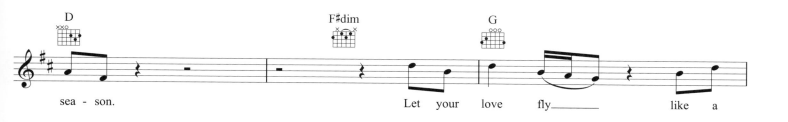

sea - son. Let your love fly_____ like a

bird on the wing___ and let your love bind you to all liv-ing things_ and let your

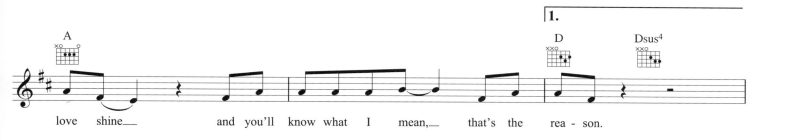

1.

love shine___ and you'll know what I mean,____ that's the rea - son.

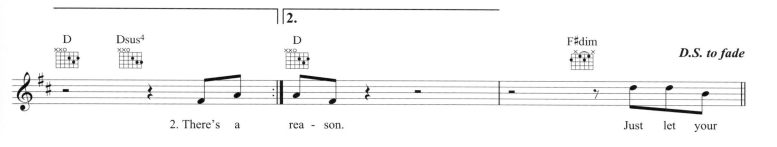

2.

D.S. to fade

2. There's a rea - son. Just let your

Little Red Rooster
Words & Music by Willie Dixon

© Copyright 1961 Hoochie Coochie Music/Arc Music Corporation, USA.
Bug Music Limited (70%)/Jewel Music Publishing Company Limited (30%).
All Rights Reserved. International Copyright Secured.

I am the lit-tle red roo-ster, too la-zy to crow to-day.

I am the lit-tle red roo-ster,

too la-zy to crow to-day.

Keep ev-'ry-thing in the farm-yard, up-set in ev-'ry way.

The dogs be-gin to bark and

hounds be-gin to howl. The dogs be-gin to bark and

hounds be-gin to howl.

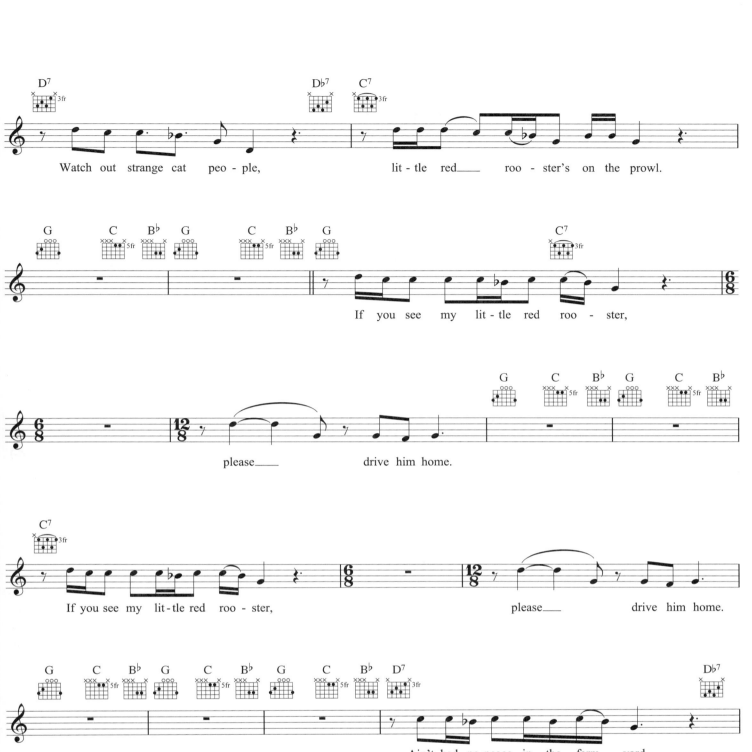

Watch out strange cat peo - ple, lit - tle red___ roo - ster's on the prowl.

If you see my lit - tle red roo - ster,

please___ drive him home.

If you see my lit - tle red roo - ster, please___ drive him home.

Ain't had no peace in the farm - yard,

since my lit - tle red___ roo - ster's been gone.

(Guitar)

Little Sister

Words & Music by
Josh Homme, Troy Van Leeuwen & Joey Castillo

© Copyright 2005 Magic Bullet Music (12.5%)/More Kick And Snare Music (7.5%)/Board Stiff Music, USA.
Universal Music Publishing Limited (80%) (administered in Germany by Universal Music Publ. GmbH).
All Rights Reserved. International Copyright Secured.

125

Live Forever
Words & Music by Noel Gallagher

© Copyright 1994 Creation Songs Limited/Oasis Music (GB).
Sony/ATV Music Publishing (UK) Limited.
All Rights Reserved. International Copyright Secured.

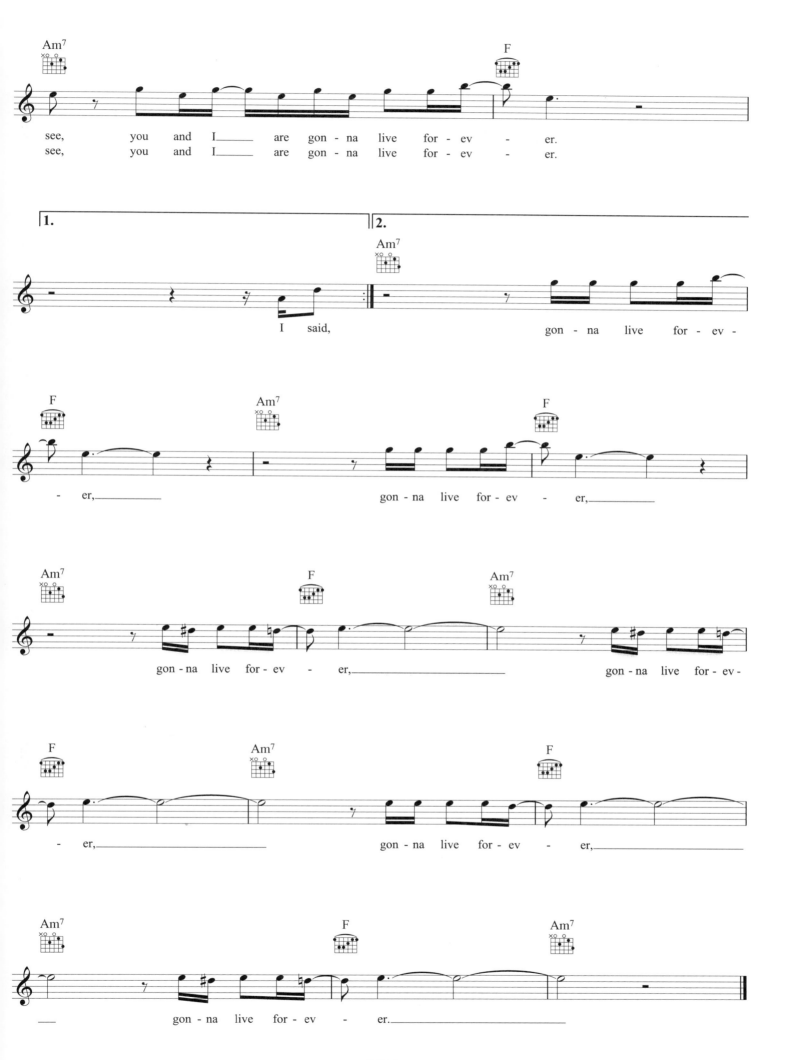

Living In The Past
Words & Music by Ian Anderson

© Copyright 1969 Ian Anderson Music Limited/Chrysalis Music Limited.
All Rights Reserved. International Copyright Secured.

The Lovecats
Words & Music by Robert Smith

© Copyright 1983 Fiction Songs Limited.
All Rights Reserved. International Copyright Secured.

1.

love - cats.
(Ba - ba ba ba ba ba ba ba. Ba___ ba ba ba ba ba ba ba.)

We missed you hissed the

love - cats.
(ba ba ba ba ba ba ba ba. Ba___ ba ba ba ba ba ba ba.)

2. We're so

2.

love - cats.

We miss you hissed the

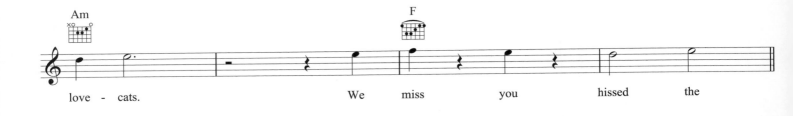

love - cats.

We miss you hissed the

love - cats.
(Ba ba ba ba ba ba ba ba. Ba___ ba ba ba ba ba ba ba.)

We___ miss you hissed the

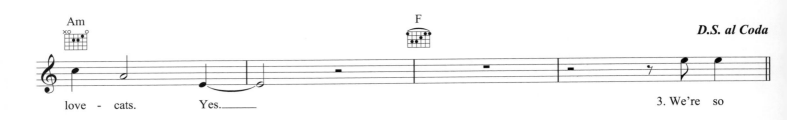

D.S. al Coda

love - cats. Yes.___

3. We're so

Coda

Hand in hand is the on - ly way to land and al - ways the right___ way round.___

— Not bro - ken in piec - es like hat - ed lit - tle mee - ces. How could we miss some -

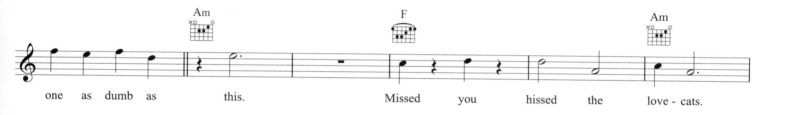

one as dumb as this. Missed you hissed the love - cats.

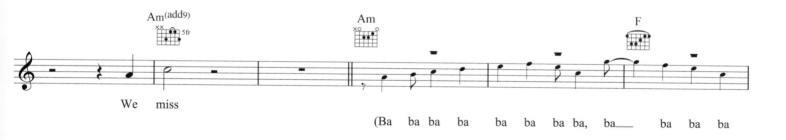

We miss

(Ba ba ba ba ba ba ba ba, ba___ ba ba ba

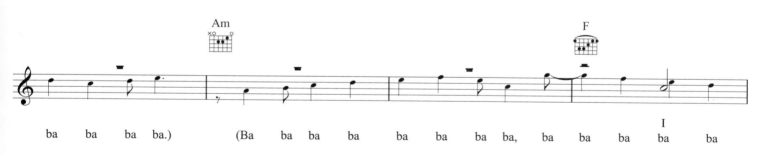

ba ba ba ba.) (Ba ba ba ba ba ba ba ba, ba ba ba ba ba ba

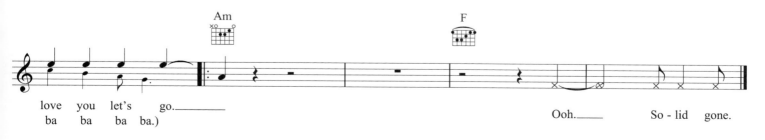

love you let's go.___
ba ba ba ba.)

Ooh.___ So - lid gone.

Many Shades Of Black

Words & Music by
Jack White & Brendan Benson

© Copyright 2008 Gladsad Music/Third String Tunes, USA.
Chrysalis Music Limited (50%)/EMI Music Publishing Limited (50%).
All Rights Reserved. International Copyright Secured.

Matthew & Son
Words & Music by Cat Stevens

© Copyright 1966 Cat Music Limited.
All Rights Reserved. International Copyright Secured.

May You Never

Words & Music by
John Martyn

© Copyright 1972 Warlock Music Limited.
Kobalt Music Publishing Limited.
All Rights Reserved. International Copyright Secured.

won't you please, won't you bear it in your mind.___ Love is a les - son to

learn in our time___ and please, won't you please, won't you bear it in mind___

___ for me. And may you bear it in mind___ for me.___

___ And may you ne - ver lose your term -

- per if you get___ in a bar - room fight,___ and may___ you

ne - ver lose your wo - man ov - er - night.___

___ May you ne - ver lay your head___ down___ with - out___

137

Miss Misery
Words & Music by Elliott Smith

© Copyright 1998 Spent Bullets Music, USA.
Universal Music Publishing MGB Limited.
All rights in Germany administered by Musik Edition Discoton GmbH (a division of Universal Music Publishing Group).
All Rights Reserved. International Copyright Secured.

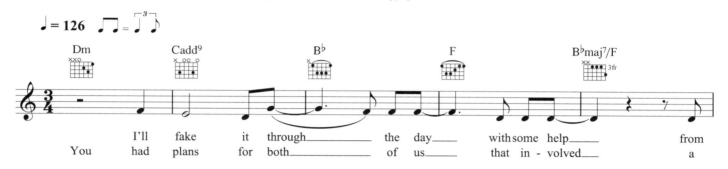

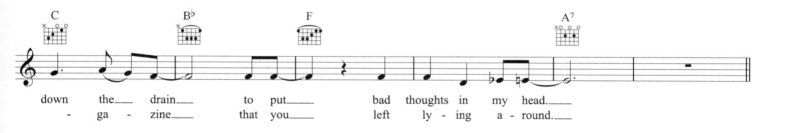

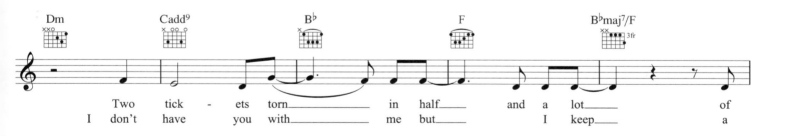

The Mercy Seat

Words by Nick Cave
Music by Nick Cave & Mick Harvey

© Copyright 1988 Mute Song.
All Rights Reserved. International Copyright Secured.

They came and took me from my home and put me in death row,
of which I'm nearly wholly innocent of.

And I'll say it again... I'm not afraid to die.

Spoken: Verse 1 see block lyric

1. And the mer-cy seat is a-wait-ing, and I think my head is burn-ing, and in a way I'm yearn-ing to be done with all this meas-ur-ing___ of truth; an eye for an eye and a tooth for a tooth. And a-ny-way___ I told the truth, and I'm not a-fraid___ to die.

Spoken: Verse 2 see block lyric

2. I hear sto-ries from the cham-ber, Christ was born in-to a man- -ger like some rag-ged strang-er died up-on the cross.___ And might I say___ it seems so fit-ting in its

143

and I'm not a-fraid to why. 7. And the mer-cy seat is wait-ing, and I think my head is burn-ing,

and in a way I'm yearn-ing to be done with all this meas-ur-ing of proof; a life for a life and a truth for a

truth. And a-ny-way there was no proof, and I'm not a-fraid to die. And the mer-cy seat is wait-ing,

and I think my head is smo-king, and in a way I'm ho-ping to be done with all these looks of dis-be-lief;

an eye for an eye and a tooth for a tooth. But a-ny-way I told the truth, and I'm not a-fraid to

die. 8. And the mer-cy seat is wait-ing, and I think my head is burn-ing, and in a way I'm yearn-ing to be
lie. *(Choruses 9 & 10 see block lyrics)*

done with all this meas-ur-ing of proof; an eye for an eye and a tooth for a tooth. And a-ny-way I told the

Play 3 times

truth, and I'm not a-fraid to (10.) lie.
(10.) and I'm a-fraid I told a

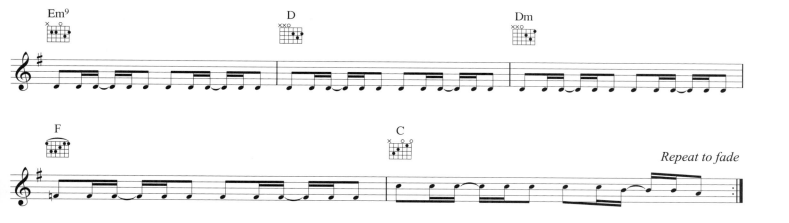

Verse 1:

I began to warm and chill to objects and their fields;

A ragged cup, a twisted mop, the face of Jesus in my soup.

Those sinister dinner deals, the meal trolley's wicked wheels,

A hooked bone rising from my food; all things either good or ungood.

Verse 2:

Interpret signs and catalogue, a blackened tooth, a scarlet frog.

The walls are bad, black bottom kind; they are the sick breath at my hind.

They are the sick breath at my hind, they are the sick breath at my hind,

They are the sick breath gathering at my hind.

Verse 3:

Like my good hand I tattooed EVIL across its brother's fist.

That filthy five! They did nothing to challenge or resist.

Verse 4:

My kill hand is called 'evil', wears a wedding band that's good;

'Tis a long suffering shackle collaring all that rebel blood.

Chorus 6:

And the mercy seat is waiting, and I think my head is burning,

And in a way I'm yearning to be done with all this measuring of proof;

An eye for an eye and a tooth for a tooth.

And anyway there was no proof and nor a motive why.

Chorus 9:

And the mercy seat is waiting, and I think my head is burning,

And in a way I'm yearning to be done with all this measuring of proof;

An eye for an eye and a tooth for a tooth.

And anyway I told the truth, but I'm not afraid to lie.

Chorus 10:

And the mercy seat is waiting, and I think my head is burning,

And in a way I'm yearning to be done with all this measuring of proof;

An eye for an eye and a tooth for a tooth.

And anyway I told the truth, and I'm afraid I told a lie.

Midlife Crisis

Words by Mike Patton

Music by Mike Patton, Roddy Bottum, Billy Gould, Jim Martin & Mike Bordin

© Copyright 1992 Vomit God/Big Thrilling Music, USA.
Universal Music Publishing Limited.
All Rights Reserved. International Copyright Secured.

A New England
Words & Music by Billy Bragg

© Copyright 1983 Universal Music Publishing MGB Limited.
All rights in Germany administered by Musik Edition Discoton GmbH (a division of Universal Music Publishing Group).
All Rights Reserved. International Copyright Secured.

Picture This

Words & Music by
Deborah Harry, Chris Stein & Jimmy Destri

© Copyright 1978 Rare Blue Music Incorporated, USA.
Chrysalis Music Limited.
All Rights Reserved. International Copyright Secured.

1. All I want___ is a room with a view:___ a sight worth see - ing, a

vis - ion of you.___ All I want is a room with a view,___ oh,___

woh,___ woh,___ woh. 2. I will give you my

fin - est hour:___ the one I spent watch-ing you show - er. I will give you

my fin - est hour,___ oh___ yeah. 3. All I want___ is a

pho - to in my wal - let; a small re-mem-brance of some-thing more so - lid. All I want

is a pic-ture of you.___ Pic-ture this: a day in De - cem - ber.

Pic - ture this: freez-ing cold wea - ther. You got clouds on your lids___ and you'd

150

be on the skids__ if it weren't__ for your job__ at the gar - age. If you could on - ly, oh____

woh, pic - ture this: a sky full of thun - der. Pic - ture this: my te - le - phone num - ber.

To Coda One and one is what I'm tell - ing__ you,_ oh yeah.

All I want_ is twen - ty twen - ty vi - sion; a to - tal por - trait with no o - mis - sions.

D.S. al Coda

All I want is a vi - sion of you,__ oh._____ If you can,

Coda tell - ing__ you;_ get a po - cket com - pu - ter, try to do what you used_ to do,_ yeah!

Please, Please, Please, Let Me Get What I Want

Words & Music by Morrissey & Johnny Marr

© Copyright 1984 Artemis Muziekuitgeverij B.V./Marr Songs Limited.
Warner/Chappell Artemis Music Limited (50%)/
Universal Music Publishing Limited (50%) (administered in Germany by Universal Music Publ. GmbH).
All Rights Reserved. International Copyright Secured.

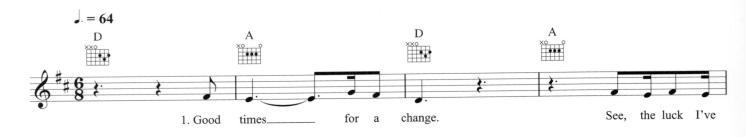

1. Good times for a change. See, the luck I've

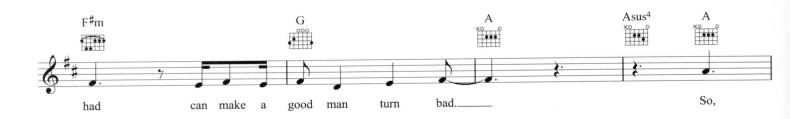

had can make a good man turn bad. So,

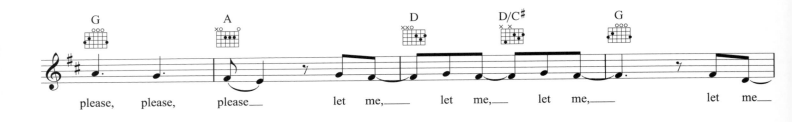

please, please, please let me, let me, let me, let me

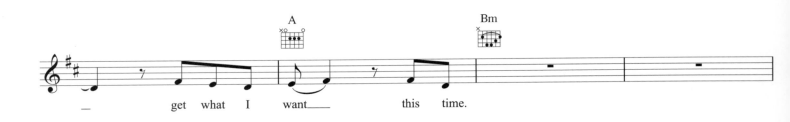

get what I want this time.

2. Have-n't had a dream

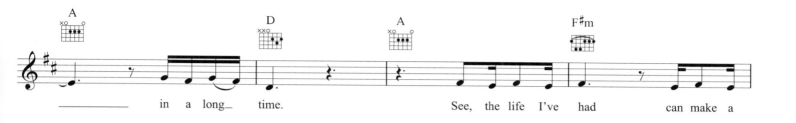

in a long___ time.   See, the life I've had   can make a

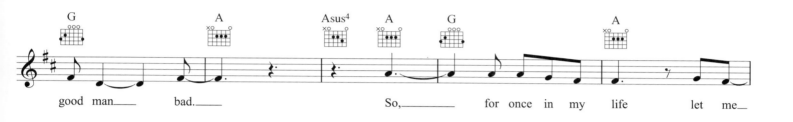

good man___ bad.___   So,___ for once in my life   let me___

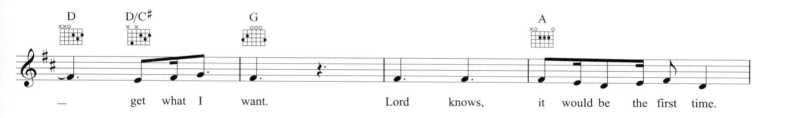

— get what I want.   Lord   knows,   it would be the first time.

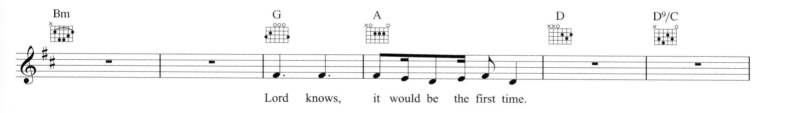

Lord   knows,   it would be the first time.

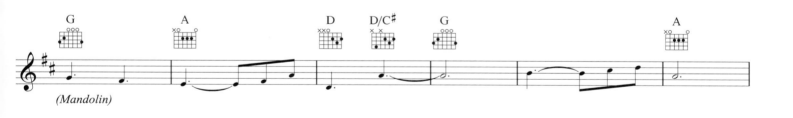

(Mandolin)

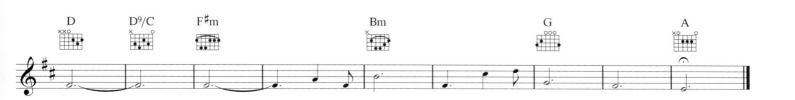

Owner Of A Lonely Heart

Words & Music by
Jon Anderson, Trevor Rabin, Chris Squire & Trevor Horn

© Copyright 1983 Tremander Songs/Opio Publishing LLC/Warner/Chappell Music Limited (75%)/
Unforgettable Songs Limited (15%)/Carlin Music Corporation (10%).
All Rights Reserved. International Copyright Secured.

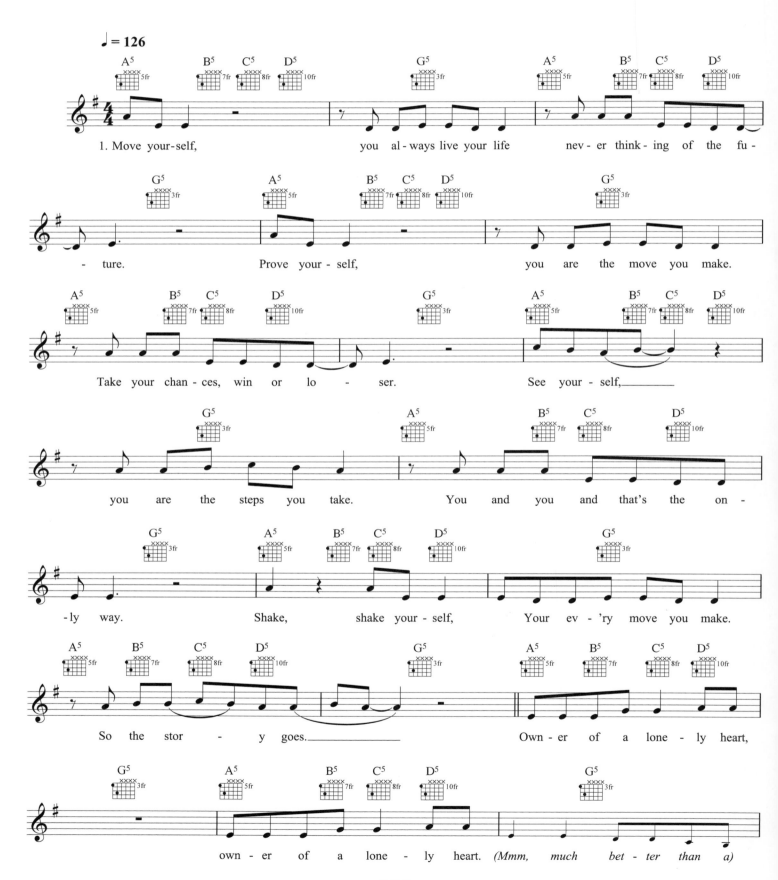

Question

Words & Music by Justin Hayward

© Copyright 1970 Tyler Music Limited.
All Rights Reserved. International Copyright Secured.

Why do we nev - er get___ an an - swer___ when we're

knock - ing at___ the door?___ Be - cause the truth is hard___ to swal-

- low,___ that's what the wall of love___ is for.___

Slower ♩ = c.72 *Fine*

1. It's not the way___ that you say___ it, when you do
(2.) si - lence of the moun - tains and the crash-

___ those things to me; it's more the way___ that you mean___ it, when you tell
- ing of the sea, there lies a land___ I once lived___ in, and she's wait-

___ me what___ will be. And when you stop and think___ a - bout___ it, you won't
- ing there___ for me. But in the grey___ of the mor - ning, my mind___

___ be -lieve___ it's true, that all___ the love___ you've been giv - ing has all
___ be - comes con - fused be - tween___ the dead___ and the sleep - ing and the road.

___ been meant___ for you. ⎫ I'm look - ing for___ some - one___ to change___ my
_ that I___ must choose. ⎭

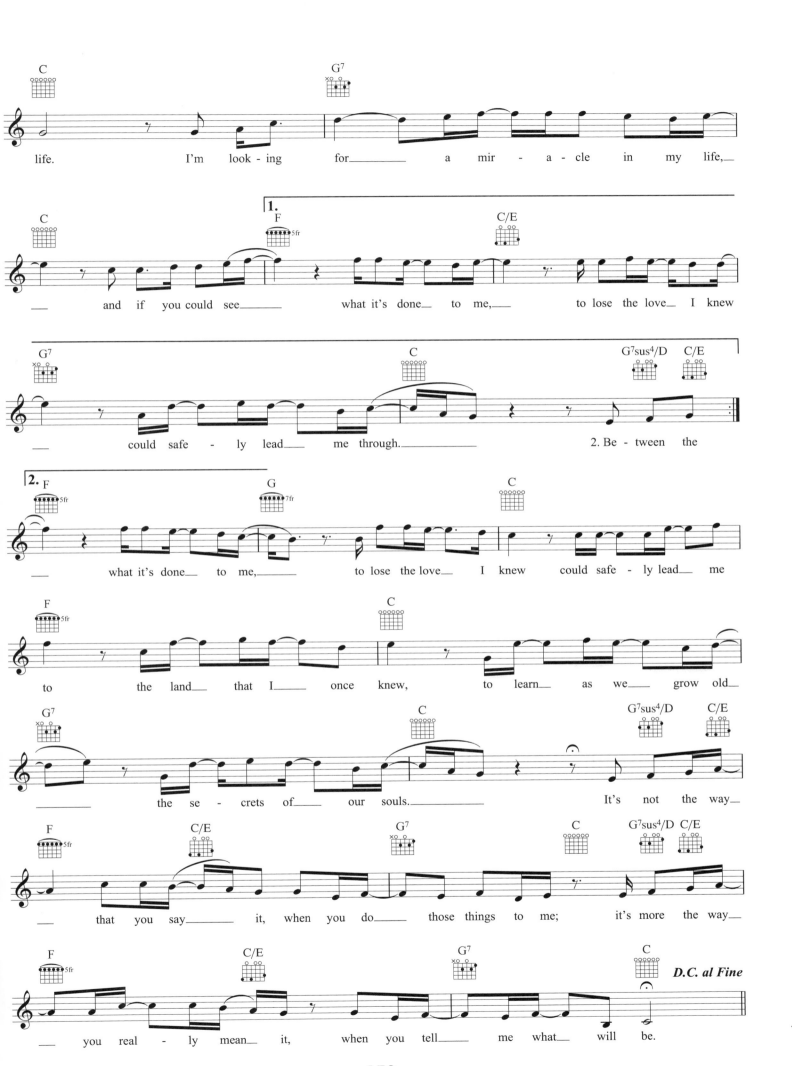

A Rainy Night In Soho
Words & Music by Shane MacGowan

© Copyright 1986 Pogue Music Limited.
Perfect Songs Limited.
All Rights Reserved. International Copyright Secured.

I took shel-ter from a show-er,____ and I stepped in - to your
I'm not sing-ing for the fu - ture,____ I'm not dream-ing of the

arms, on a rain-y night__ in So - ho,____
past, I'm not talk - ing of the first time,____

the wind was whist-ling all its charms.
I nev - er think a - bout____ the last.

Now, the song is near-ly o - ver,____ we__ may nev-er find out what it

means. Still,____ there's a light I hold be - fore me,____

you're the meas-ure of my dreams, the meas-ure____ of my dreams.

Repeat to fade

161

Ride A White Swan
Words & Music by Marc Bolan

© Copyright 1970 Westminster Music Limited.
All Rights Reserved. International Copyright Secured.

Original Key: G♯ (to match original use a Capo, 4th fret)

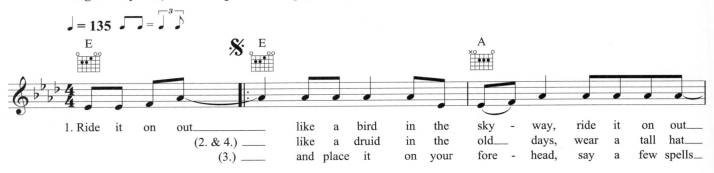

1. Ride it on out_____ like a bird in the sky - way, ride it on out
(2. & 4.) ___ like a druid in the old___ days, wear a tall hat
(3.) ___ and place it on your fore - head, say a few spells___

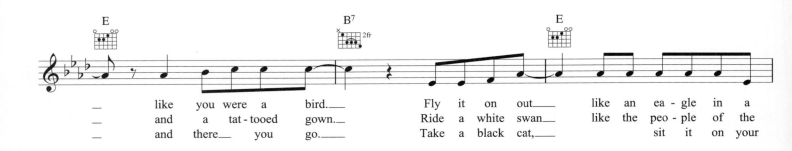

___ like you were a bird.___ Fly it on out_____ like an ea - gle in a
___ and a tat - tooed gown.___ Ride a white swan_____ like the peo - ple of the
___ and there___ you go.___ Take a black cat,___ sit it on your

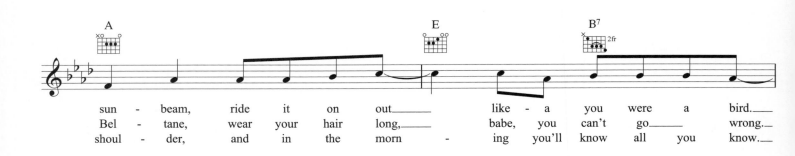

sun - beam, ride it on out_____ like - a you were a bird.
Bel - tane, wear your hair long,___ babe, you can't go___ wrong.
shoul - der, and in the morn - ing you'll know all you know.___

1, 2. **3.**

To Coda ✛

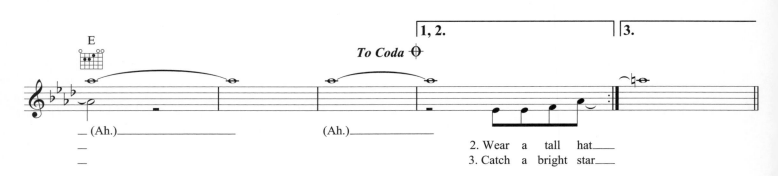

_ (Ah.)___ (Ah.)___
_ 2. Wear a tall hat___
_ 3. Catch a bright star___

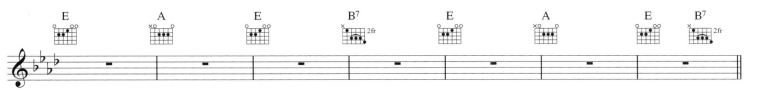

D.S. al Coda

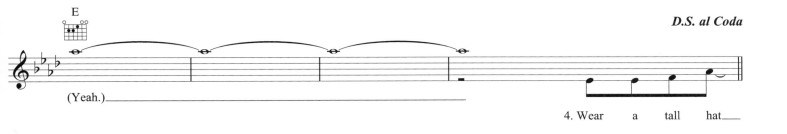

(Yeah.)_____

4. Wear a tall hat___

Coda

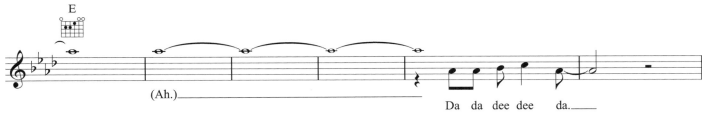

(Ah.)_____

Da da dee dee da.___

Da da dee dee da.___ Da da dee dee da.___ Da da dee dee da.___

Repeat to fade

___ Da da dee dee da.___ Da da dee dee da.___ Da da dee dee da.___

Rock 'n' Roll Damnation

Words & Music by
Angus Young & Malcolm Young

© Copyright 1978 J. Albert & Son Pty. Limited.
All Rights Reserved. International Copyright Secured.

And it's a
bite of what you've got, and it's a } rock 'n' roll___ dam - na - tion,

Ma's own whip - ping boy.___ Rock 'n' roll___ dam - na - tion,

1.

take your chance,___ while you still___ got the choice.___ *(Guitar riff)*

2.

2. You ___ *(Guitar)*

(Oh, it's a hard life.)

(Dam - na - tion!) They're put - ting us down!_ (Dam -

-na - tion!)__ All__ o - ver town!__ *(Dam - na - tion!)*__ 'Cause you're way__

__ out of reach!__ Liv - in' on the streets you got to prac - tise what you preach. Well, it's a

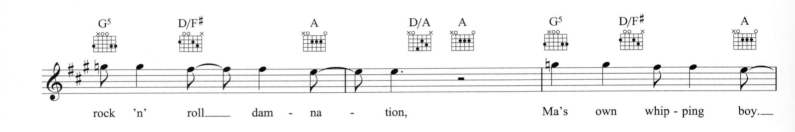

rock 'n' roll__ dam - na - tion, Ma's own whip - ping boy.__

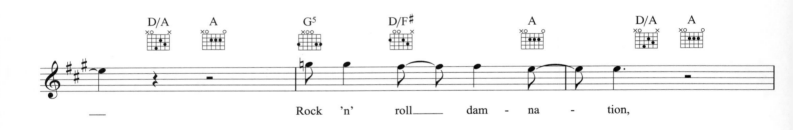

__ Rock 'n' roll__ dam - na - tion,

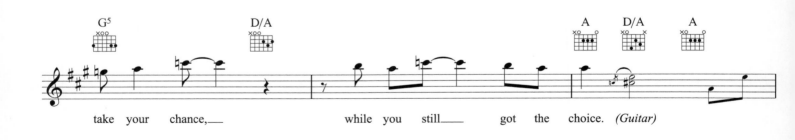

take your chance,__ while you still__ got the choice. *(Guitar)*

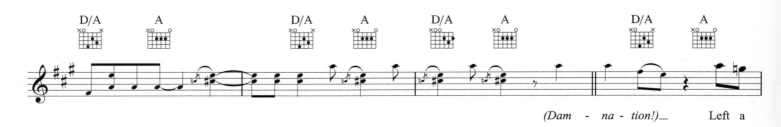

*(Dam - na - tion!)*__ Left a

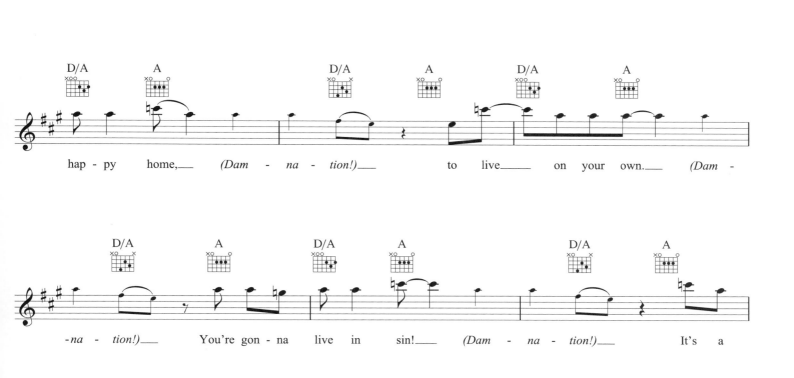

hap - py home,___ (Dam - na - tion!) ___ to live___ on your own.___ (Dam -

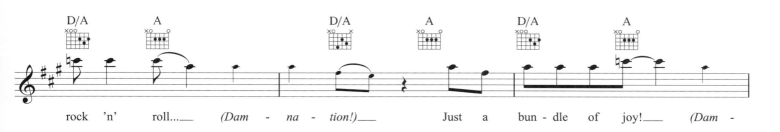

-na - tion!) ___ You're gon - na live in sin! ___ (Dam - na - tion!) ___ It's a

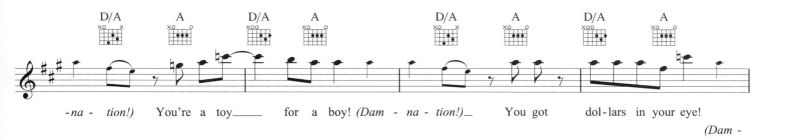

rock 'n' roll...___ (Dam - na - tion!) ___ Just a bun - dle of joy! ___ (Dam -

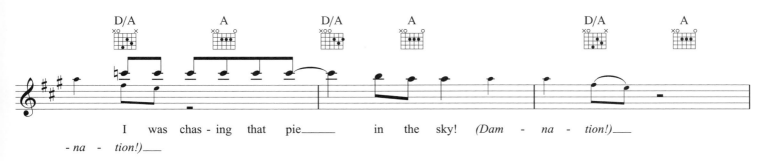

-na - tion!) You're a toy___ for a boy! (Dam - na - tion!)__ You got dol - lars in your eye!

(Dam -

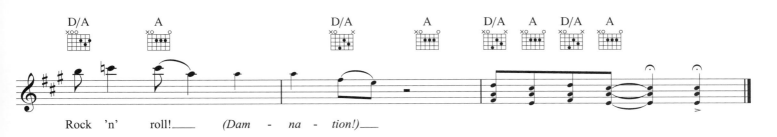

I was chas - ing that pie___ in the sky! (Dam - na - tion!)___

-na - tion!)___

Rock 'n' roll!___ (Dam - na - tion!)___

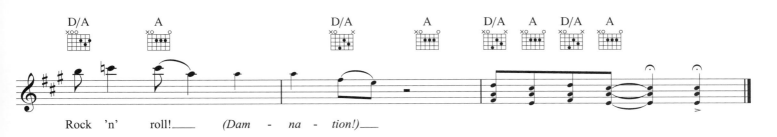

Rock The Casbah

Words & Music by The Clash

© Copyright 1982 Nineden Limited/Universal Music Publishing Limited.
All rights in Germany administered by Universal Music Publ. GmbH.
All Rights Reserved. International Copyright Secured.

King called up his jet fight-ers, he said you'd bet-ter earn your pay!___ Drop your

bombs be-tween the min-a-rets, down the Cas-bah way.___ As

soon as the Sha-ria was chauf-fered out of there, the jet pi-lots tuned___ to the

cock-pit ra-dio blare. As soon as the Sha-ria was out of their hair, the jet fight-ers wailed.___

D.S. al Coda ⊕ *Coda*

___ Sha - rock the Cas-bah. Sha-ria___ don't___ like it,___

(He

rock-in' the Cas-bah, rock the Cas-bah. Sha-

thinks it's not kosh-er.)

(Fade to end)

- ria___ don't___ like it,___ rock-in' the Cas-bah, rock the Cas-bah. Sha-

(Fun-da-men-tal-ly can't take it.)

- ria___ don't___ like it,___ Rock-in' the Cas-bah, rock the Cas-bah.

(You know he real-ly hates it.)

169

Rocky Mountain Way

Words & Music by
Joe Walsh, Kenny Passarelli, Roche Grace & Joe Vitale

© Copyright 1973 Barn Storm Music Incorporated/Belkin Music/Duchess Music Corporation, USA.
Universal/MCA Music Limited.
All rights in Germany administered by Universal/MCA Music Publ. GmbH.
All Rights Reserved. International Copyright Secured.

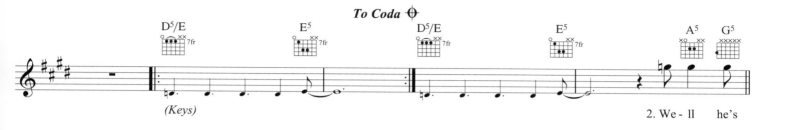

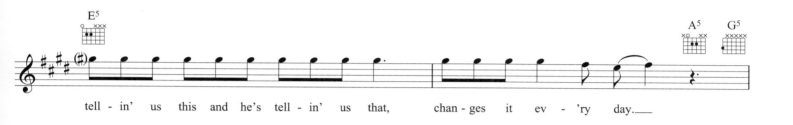

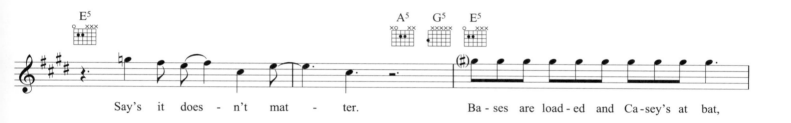

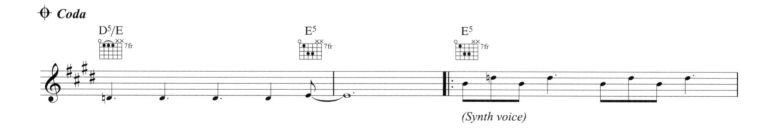

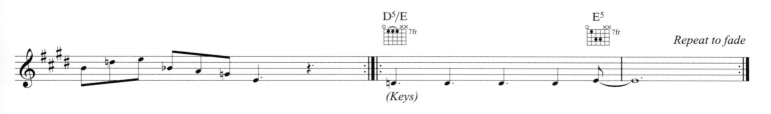

Ruby, Don't Take Your Love To Town

Words & Music by Mel Tillis

© Copyright 1966 Cedarwood Publishing Company Incorporated, USA.
Universal Music Publishing Limited.
All rights in Germany administered by Universal Music Publ. GmbH.
All Rights Reserved. International Copyright Secured.

go and do my pa - tri - o - tic chore.   And

yes it's true   that I'm not the man I used to be.

Oh, Ru - - by,   I still

need some com - pan - y.   3. It's

hard to love a man whose legs are bent and par - al - yzed,

and the wants and the needs of a wom-an your age,

Ru - by, I re - al - ise.   But it

won't be long I've heard them say, un - til I'm not a - round.

173

Oh, Ru - - by,_____

don't take your love to town.

4. She's

leav-ing now,__ 'cause I just heard the slam -ming of__ the door,__

the way I know I've heard it slam one - hun-dred times__ be - fore.

And if I could move_ I'd get my gun and put her in the ground.__

Oh, Ru - -

- by,_____

don't take your love to town.

1.

Oh ___ for God's sakes, turn a-round.

2.

174

She's Not There
Words & Music by Rod Argent

© Copyright 1964 Marquis Music Company Limited.
All Rights Reserved. International Copyright Secured.

Smile

Words & Music by
Lily Allen, Iyiola Babalola, Darren Lewis & Jackie Mittoo

© Copyright 2006 Universal Music Publishing Limited (50%) (administered in Germany by Universal Music Publ. GmbH)/
Sparta Florida Music Group Limited (50%).
All Rights Reserved. International Copyright Secured.

1. When you first left me, I was want - ing
(2.) - ev - er you see me, you say that you

more, but you were do - ing that girl next door; what'd you do that
want me back, and I tell you it don't mean jack; no, it don't mean

for? When you first left me, I did - n't know what to
jack. I could - n't stop laugh - ing; no, I just could n't

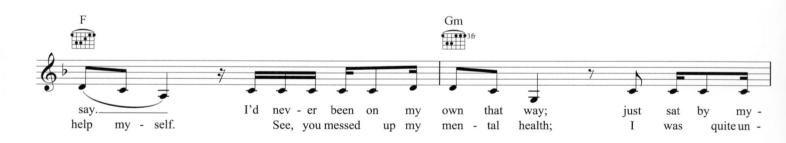

say. I'd nev - er been on my own that way; just sat by my -
help my - self. See, you messed up my men - tal health; I was quite un -

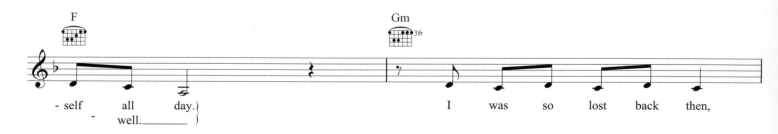

- self all day.) I was so lost back then,
well.

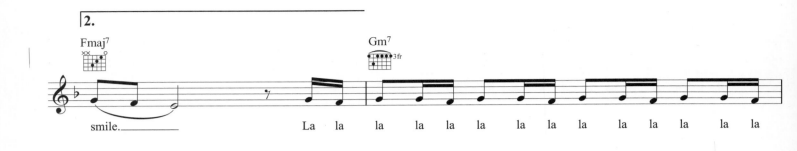

2.

Fmaj7   Gm7

smile.   La   la   la   la   la   la   la   la   la   la   la   la   la   la

Fmaj7   Gm7

la   la   la   la   la   la   la   la   la   la   la   la   la   la   la   la   la   la   la   la   la

Fmaj7   Gm7   Fmaj7

     la.   At   first,   when I   see   you   cry,   it makes me

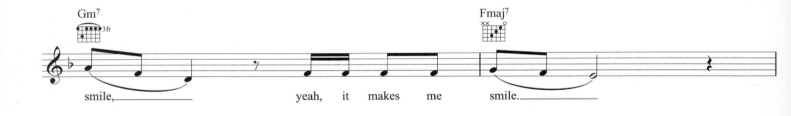

Gm7   Fmaj7

smile,   yeah, it makes   me   smile.

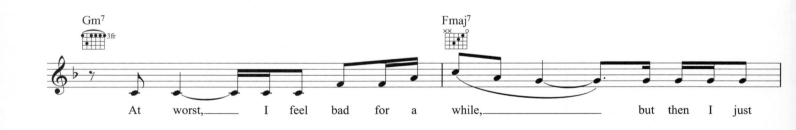

Gm7   Fmaj7

At   worst,   I feel bad for   a   while,   but then I   just

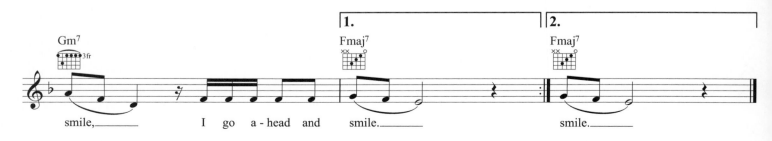

1.   **2.**

Gm7   Fmaj7   Fmaj7

smile,   I   go a-head and   smile.   smile.

Something's Gotten Hold Of My Heart

Words & Music by
Roger Cook & Roger Greenaway

© Copyright 1967 Cookaway Music Limited/Maribus Music Limited.
Universal/Dick James Music Limited.
All rights in Germany administered by Universal Music Publ. GmbH.
All Rights Reserved. International Copyright Secured.

Original key: Gm (to match the original use a Capo, 3rd fret)

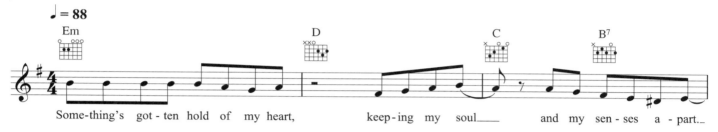

Some-thing's got-ten hold of my heart, keep-ing my soul___ and my sen-ses a-part.___

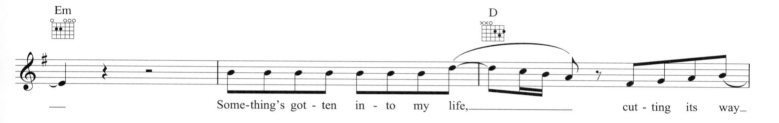

___ Some-thing's got-ten in-to my life,___ cut-ting its way___

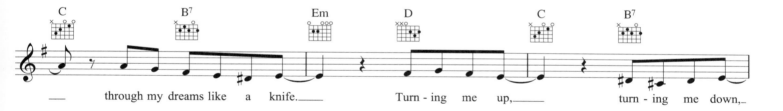

___ through my dreams like a knife.___ Turn-ing me up,___ turn-ing me down,___

___ ma-king me smile___ and ma-king me frown.

In a world that was war,___ I once lived in a time___

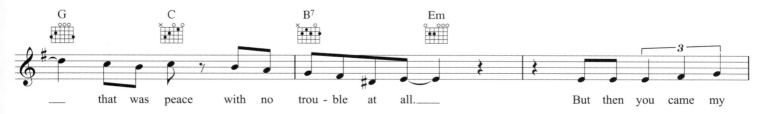

___ that was peace with no trou-ble at all.___ But then you came my

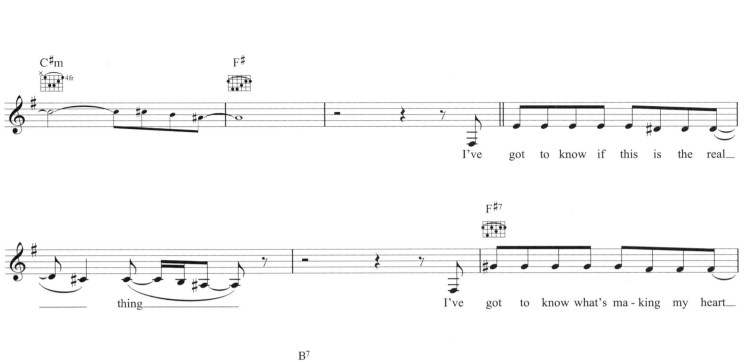

I've got to know if this is the real

thing. I've got to know what's ma-king my heart

sing, oh - oh - oh, ye - e - e - e - e - eah. You

smile and I am lost for a life - time, each min - ute spent with you is the right

time. Ev' - ry hour, yeah! Ev' - ry day, yeah, you

touch me and my mind goes a - stray, and ba - -

D.S. al Fine to fade

- by, yeah! And ba - - by, yeah!

Space Oddity
Words & Music by David Bowie

© Copyright 1969 Onward Music Limited.
All Rights Reserved. International Copyright Secured.

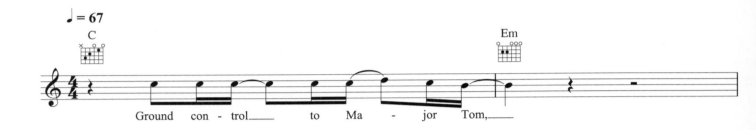

Ground con-trol___ to Ma-jor Tom,___

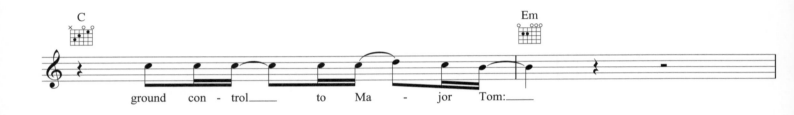

ground con-trol___ to Ma-jor Tom:___

Take your pro-tein pills and put your hel-met on.___ Ground con-trol___ to Ma-jor Tom:___

Spoken: Ten, Nine,

Com-men-cing count down: En-gines on.

Eight, Seven, Six, Five, Four, Three,

(Space craft lift-off effects)

Check ig-ni-tion and may God's love be with you.

Two, One, Lift off!

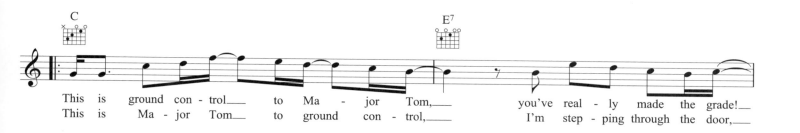

This is ground con-trol___ to Ma - jor Tom,___ you've real - ly made the grade!
This is Ma - jor Tom___ to ground con - trol,___ I'm step - ping through the door,___

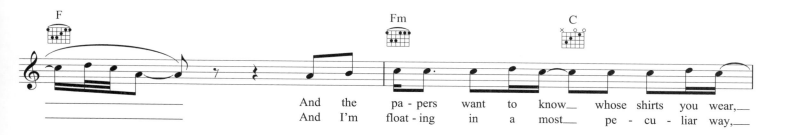

And the pa - pers want to know___ whose shirts you wear,___
And I'm float - ing in a most___ pe - cu - liar way,___

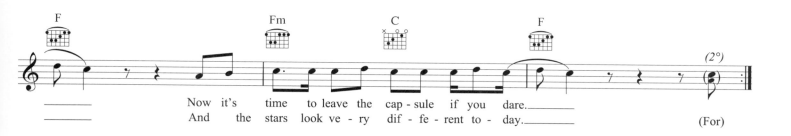

Now it's time to leave the cap - sule if you dare.___
And the stars look ve - ry dif - fe - rent to - day.___

(2°)
(For)

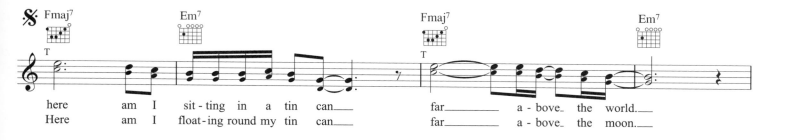

here am I sit - ting in a tin can___ far___ a - bove___ the world.___
Here am I float - ing round my tin can___ far___ a - bove___ the moon.___

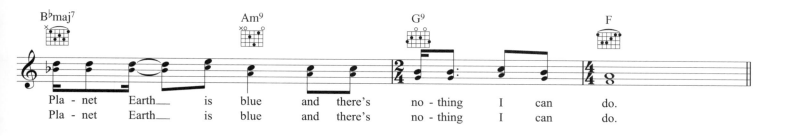

Pla - net Earth___ is blue and there's no - thing I can do.
Pla - net Earth___ is blue and there's no - thing I can do.

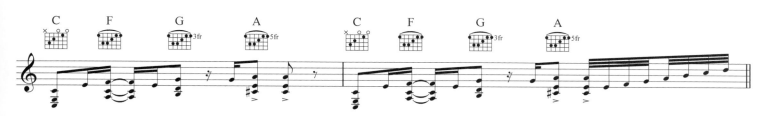

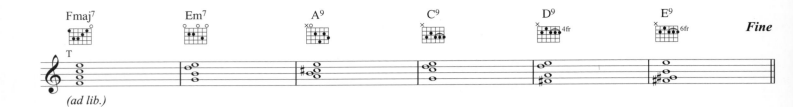

Fine

(ad lib.)

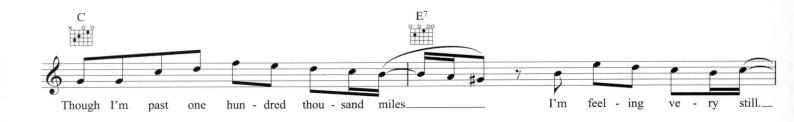

Though I'm past one hun - dred thou - sand miles_____ I'm feel - ing ve - ry still.__

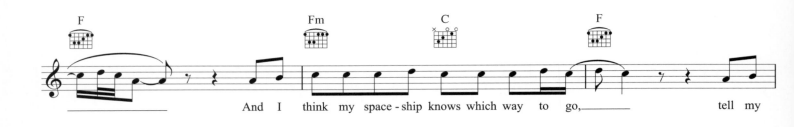

_____ And I think my space - ship knows which way to go,_____ tell my

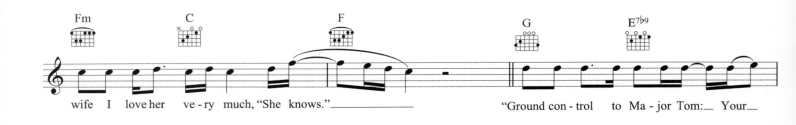

wife I love her ve - ry much, "She knows."_____ "Ground con - trol to Ma - jor Tom:__ Your__

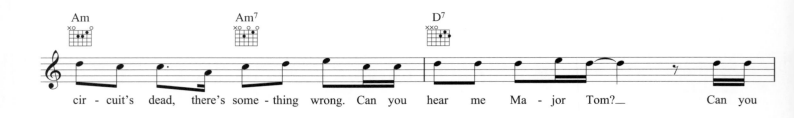

cir - cuit's dead, there's some - thing wrong. Can you hear me Ma - jor Tom?__ Can you

D.S. al Fine

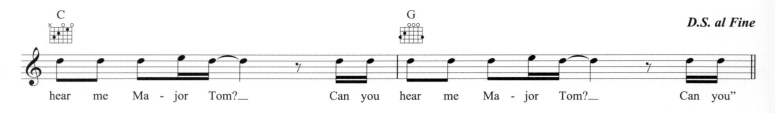

hear me Ma - jor Tom?__ Can you hear me Ma - jor Tom?__ Can you"

184

Substitute

Words & Music by Pete Townshend

© Copyright 1966 Fabulous Music Limited.
All Rights Reserved. International Copyright Secured.

♩ = 140

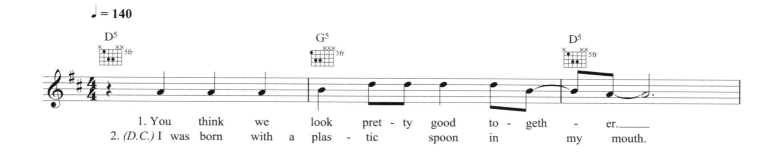

1. You think we look pret - ty good to - geth - er.
2. *(D.C.)* I was born with a plas - tic spoon in my mouth.

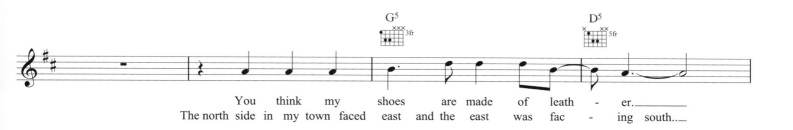

You think my shoes are made of leath - er.
The north side in my town faced east and the east was fac - ing south...

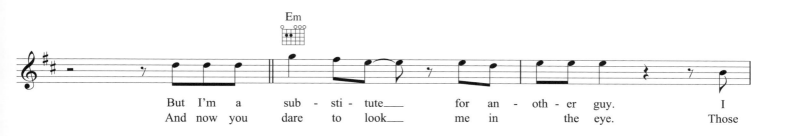

But I'm a sub - sti - tute___ for an - oth - er guy. I
And now you dare to look___ me in the eye. Those

look pret - ty tall but my heels are high. The sim - ple things you see are all
croco - dile tears are what you cry. It's a gen - u - ine prob - lem. You

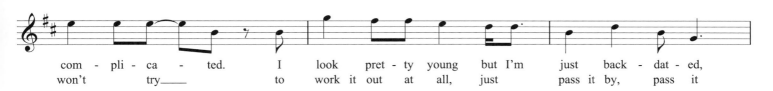

com - pli - ca - ted. I look pret - ty young but I'm just back - dat - ed,
won't try___ to work it out at all, just pass it by, pass it

yeah._____
by._____

To Coda

1. Sub - sti - tute your lies for fact. I
(Sub - sti - tute
2. Sub - sti - tute me for him.

see right through your plas - tic Mac. I look all white__ but my
sub - sti - tute
Sub - sti - tute my Coke for gin. Sub - sti - tute you

Dad was black.____ My fine look - in' suit's real - ly made out of sack.__
for my mum.____ At

1.

2.

_____ least I'll get my wash - ing

N.C.

done._____

1.

2.

I'm a sub - sti - tute____ for an-

-oth - er guy.___ I look pret - ty tall but my heels are high.___ The

sim - ple things you see are all com - pli - cat - ed. I look pret - ty young but I'm

A⁵

D.C. al Coda

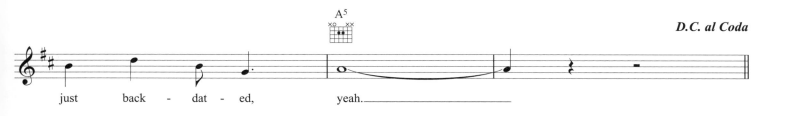

just back - dat - ed, yeah.___

 Coda

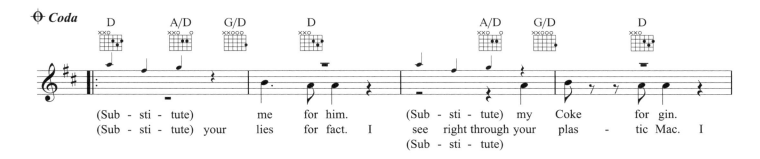

(Sub - sti - tute) me for him. (Sub - sti - tute) my Coke for gin.
(Sub - sti - tute) your lies for fact. I see right through your plas - tic Mac. I
(Sub - sti - tute)

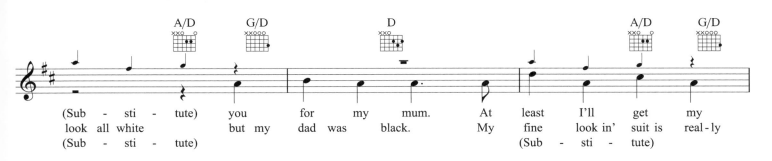

(Sub - sti - tute) you for my mum. At least I'll get my
look all white but my dad was black. My fine look in' suit is real - ly
(Sub - sti - tute) (Sub - sti - tute)

1. **2.**

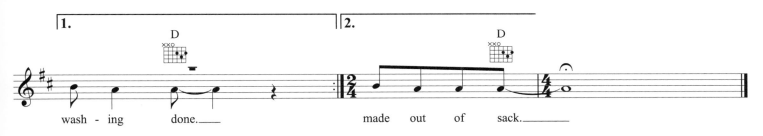

wash - ing done.___ made out of sack.___

187

The Spirit Of Radio

Words by Neil Peart
Music by Geddy Lee & Alex Lifeson

© Copyright 1980 Core Music Publishing, Canada.
Carlin Music Corporation.
All Rights Reserved. International Copyright Secured.

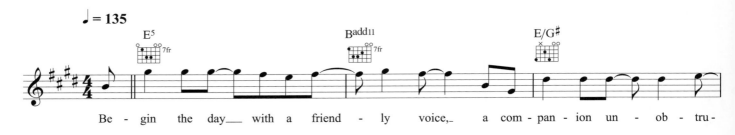

Be - gin the day___ with a friend - ly voice,___ a com - pan - ion un - ob - tru -

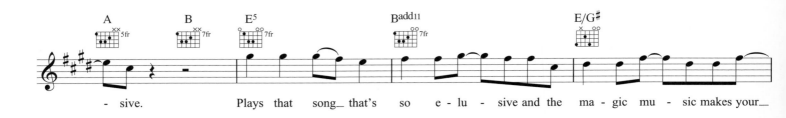

- sive. Plays that song___ that's so e - lu - sive and the ma - gic mu - sic makes your___

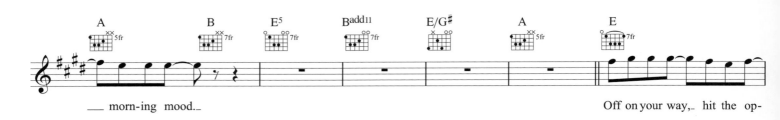

___ morn - ing mood.___ Off on your way,___ hit the op-

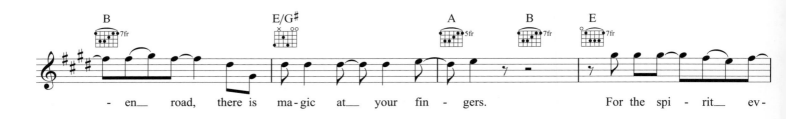

- en___ road, there is ma - gic at___ your fin - gers. For the spi - rit___ ev-

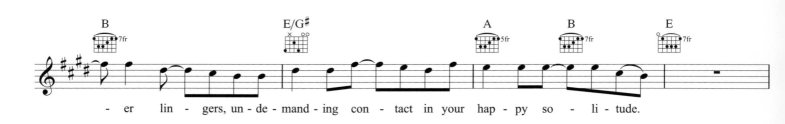

- er lin - gers, un - de - mand - ing con - tact in your hap - py so - li - tude.

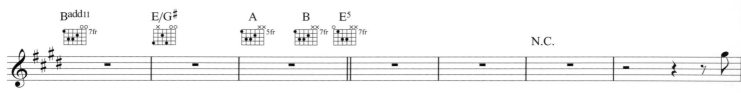

In-

-te - gri - ty,___ yeah.

In - vi - si - ble air - ways crack - le with life,___

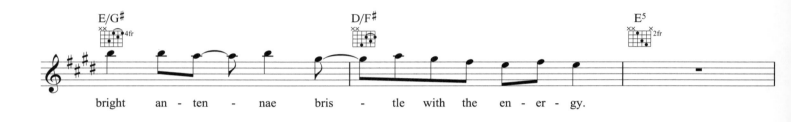

bright an - ten - nae bris - tle with the en - er - gy.

E - mo - tion - al feed - back on a time - less wave - length, bear - ing a gift___ be - yond___

price: al - most___ free.

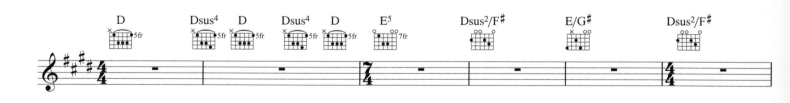

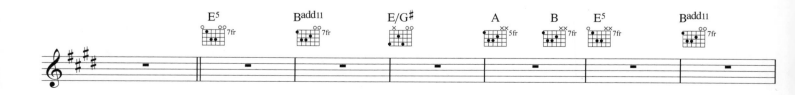

190

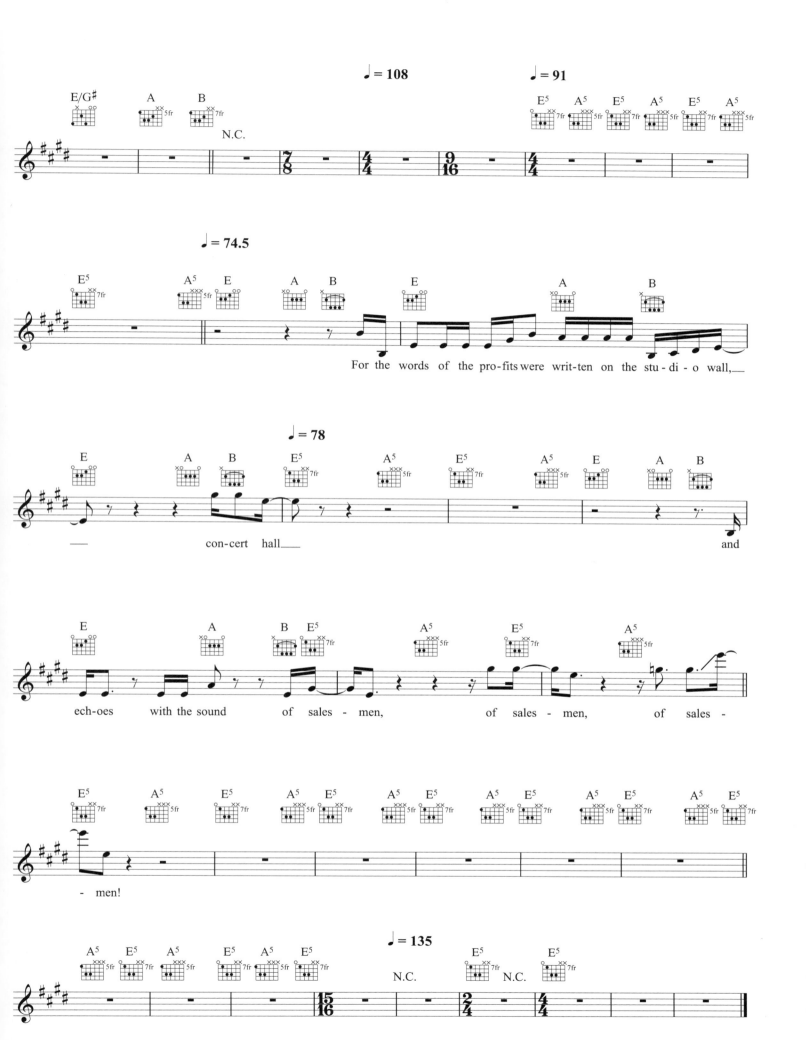

Stop Your Sobbing
Words & Music by Ray Davies

© Copyright 1964 Edward Kassner Music Company Limited.
All Rights Reserved. International Copyright Secured.

makes, makes-ah me want,____ to take you in my arms and tell you to stop all your

sob - bing.____

Ah ah-ah ah Ah ah-ah ah Ah-ah ah Ah ah-ah ah Ah ah-ah ah Ah

ah-ah ah. There's one thing you got to do,____ to make me still___ want you.___

____ And there's one thing you got to know,____ to make me want___ you so;___

___ got-ta stop sob-bing oh-oh. Got-ta stop sob-bing oh-oh. Yeah, yeah, stop stop

stop stop. Got-ta stop sob-bing oh-oh. Got-ta stop sob-bing oh-oh. Stop stop

Repeat to fade

stop stop. Got-ta stop sob-bing oh-oh. Got-ta stop sob-bing oh-oh. Stop stop stop stop. Got-ta stop sob-bing oh-oh.

Street Life
Words & Music by Bryan Ferry

© Copyright 1973 EG Music Limited/BMG Songs Limited.
All Rights Reserved. International Copyright Secured.

Strutter

Words & Music by
Paul Stanley & Gene Simmons

© Copyright 1974 Hori Productions America Incorporated/Cafe Americana/Gladwyne Music Publishing Corporation, USA.
Universal Music Publishing Limited.
All rights in Germany administered by Universal Music Publ. GmbH.
All Rights Reserved. International Copyright Secured.

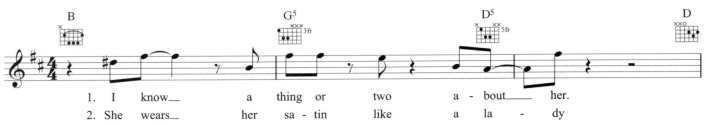

1. I know a thing or two a-bout her.
2. She wears her sa-tin like a la-dy

I know she'll on-ly make you cry.
She gets her way just like a child

She'll let you
You take her

walk the street be-side her. Ooh.
home and she says, "May-be, ba-by

But when she walks she'll pass you by.
She takes you down and drives you wild.

Ev-'ry-bo-dy says she's look-in' good,

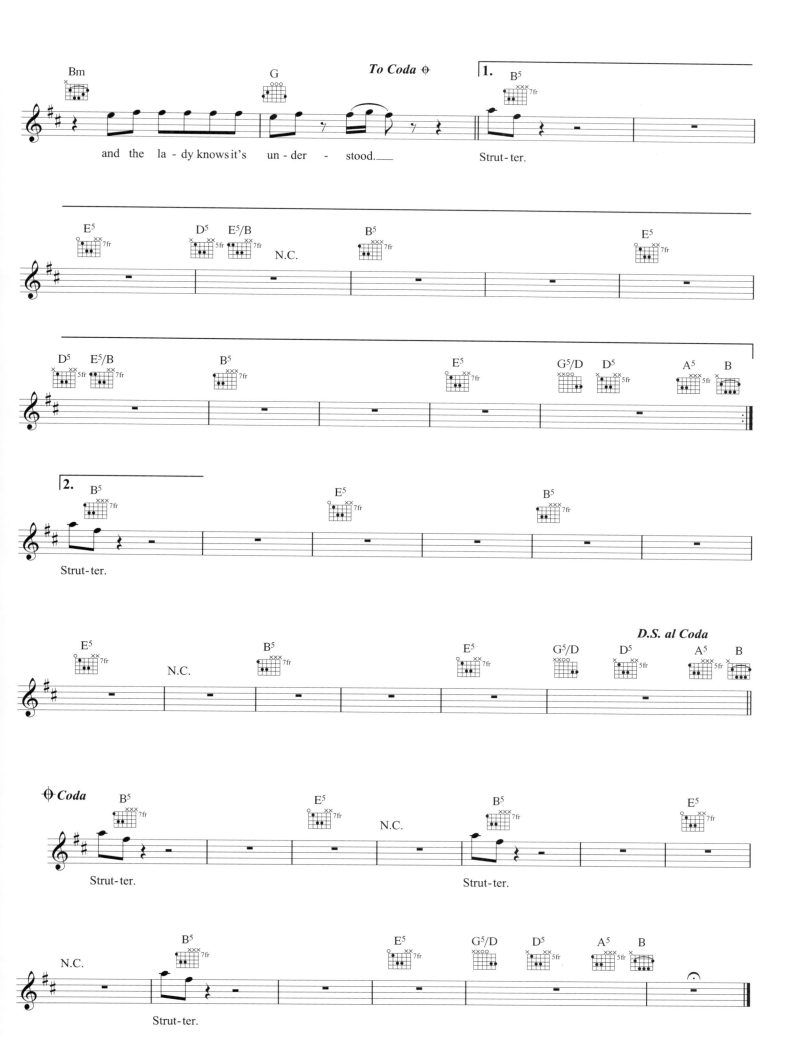

and the la - dy knows it's un - der - stood.____ Strut - ter.

Strut - ter.

Strut - ter. Strut - ter.

Strut - ter.

Sugar Man
Words & Music by Sixto Diaz Rodriguez

© Copyright 1970 Interior Music Corporation, USA.
Universal/MCA Music Limited.
All rights in Germany administered by Universal/MCA Music Publ. GmbH.
All Rights Reserved. International Copyright Secured.

it, it had turned to dead black coal.

Sil - ver mag - ic ships you car - ry, jum - pers, coke, sweet Mar - y Jane.

Sug - ar man, you're the ans -

- wer that makes my ques - tions dis - ap - pear. Sug - ar man,

'cause I'm wear - y of those doub - le games I hear.

Sug - ar man, sug - ar man, sug - ar man, sug - ar man,

sug - ar man, sug - ar man, sug - ar man.

The Sun Ain't Gonna Shine Anymore

**Words & Music by
Bob Crewe & Bob Gaudio**

© Copyright 1965 Longitude Music Company/Seasons Four Music, USA.
EMI Music Publishing (WP) Limited (50%)/EMI Music Publishing Limited (50%).
All Rights Reserved. International Copyright Secured.

1. Lone - li - ness_____ is a cloak you___ wear,___

a deep shade of blue, is___ al - ways there.___

The sun ain't gon - na shine an - y - more, the moon ain't gon - na rise in the___

___ sky.___ The tears are al - ways cloud - ing___ your eyes_____ when you're with-

- out_____ love,_____ ba - - - by.___

2. Emp - ti - ness_____ is a place you're___ in.

With noth - ing___ to lose, but no more___ to___ win.___

Sunny Afternoon
Words & Music by Ray Davies

© Copyright 1966 Davray Music Limited.
Carlin Music Corporation.
All Rights Reserved. International Copyright Secured.

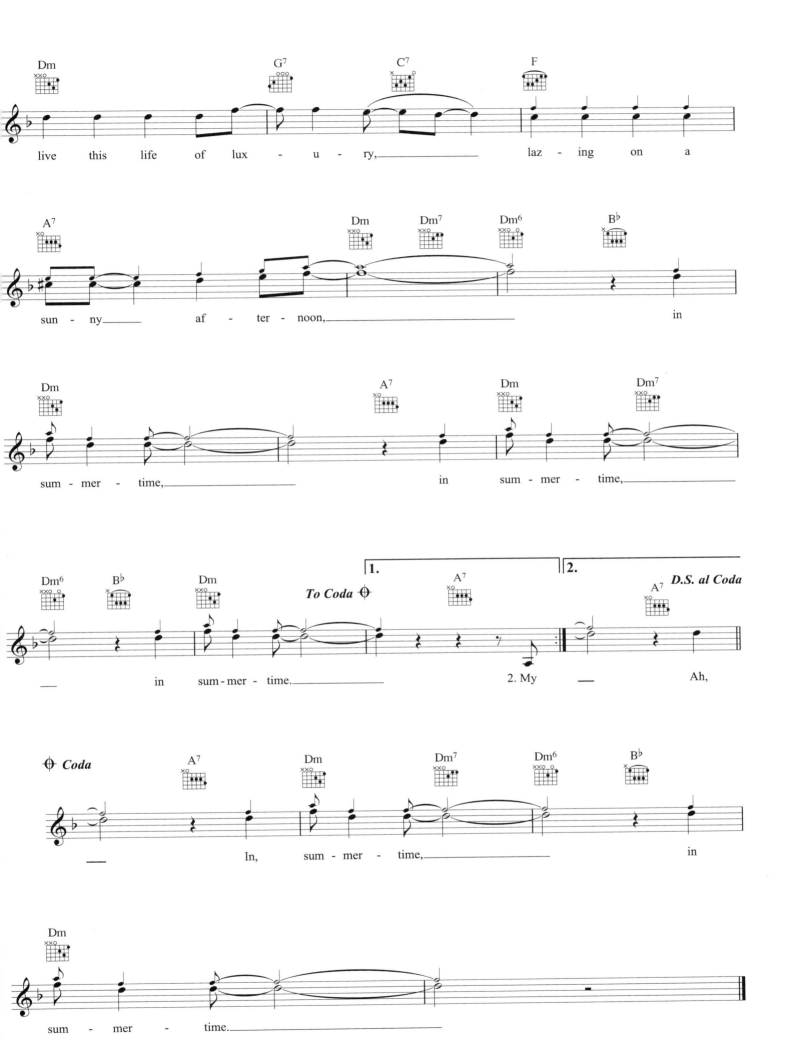

Sweet Disposition

Words & Music by
Lorenzo Sillitto & Abby Mandagi

© Copyright 2009 Imagem Music.
All Rights Reserved. International Copyright Secured.

Time To Pretend

Words & Music by
Words & Music by Andrew Vanwyngarden & Benjamin Goldwasser

© Copyright 2008 Universal Music Publishing Limited.
All rights in Germany administered by Universal Music Publ. GmbH.
All Rights Reserved. International Copyright Secured.

1. I'm feel-ing rough, I'm feel-ing raw, I'm in the prime of my life.
2. I'll miss the play-grounds and the an-i-mals and dig-ging up worms.

Let's make some mu-sic, make some mon-ey, find some mod-els for wives.
I'll miss the com-fort of my moth-er and the weight of the world.

I'll move to Par-is, shoot some her-o-in and fuck with the stars.
I'll miss my sis-ter, miss my fa-ther, miss my dog and my home.

You man the is-land and the co-caine and the el-e-gant cars.
Yeah, I'll miss the bore-dom and the free-dom and the time spent a-lone.

But

This is our de-ci-sion, to live fast and die young. We've got the vi-sion,
there is real-ly noth-ing, noth-ing we can do. Love must be for-got-ten,

now let's have some fun.
life can al-ways start a-new.

Times Like These

Words & Music by
Dave Grohl, Taylor Hawkins, Nate Mendel & Chris Shiflett

© Copyright 2002 M.J.-Twelve Music/Flying Earform Music/EMI Virgin Songs Incorporated/Living Under A Rock Music/I Love The Punk Rock Music, USA.
EMI Virgin Music Limited (75%)/Universal/MCA Music Limited (25%) (administered in Germany by Universal/MCA Music Publ. GmbH).
All Rights Reserved. International Copyright Secured.

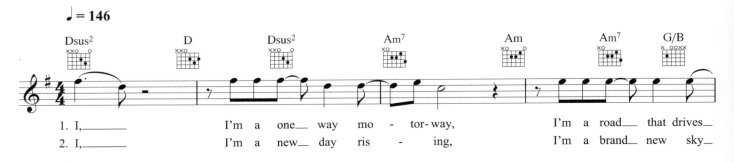

1. I,_____ I'm a one way mo-tor-way, I'm a road_ that drives
2. I,_____ I'm a new day ris-ing, I'm a brand_ new sky

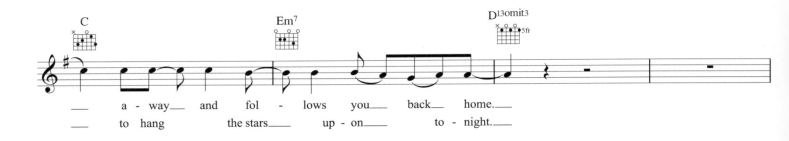

_ a - way_ and fol-lows you_ back_ home._
_ to hang the stars_ up - on_ to - night._

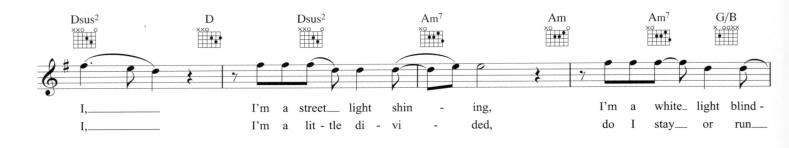

I,_____ I'm a street_ light shin-ing, I'm a white_ light blind-
I,_____ I'm a lit-tle di-vi-ded, do I stay_ or run

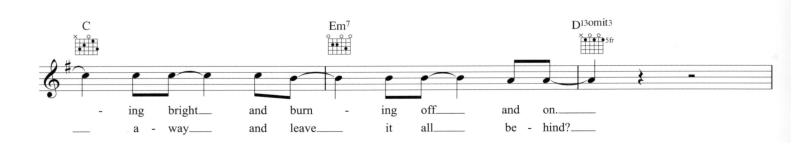

- ing bright_ and burn-ing off_ and on._
_ a - way_ and leave_ it all_ be - hind?_

Uh, It's times_ like these_ you learn_

Try A Little Tenderness

Words & Music by
Harry Woods, Jimmy Campbell & Reg Connelly

© Copyright 1932 & 1960 Campbell Connelly & Company Limited.
All Rights Reserved. International Copyright Secured.

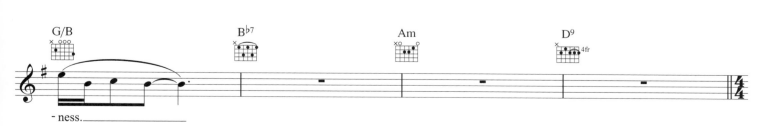

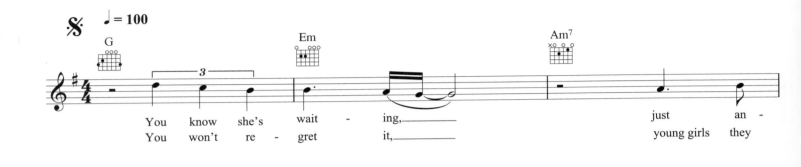

You know she's wait - ing,_____ just an -
You won't re - gret it,_____ young girls they

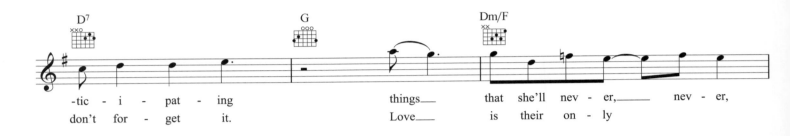

-tic - i - pat - ing things___ that she'll nev - er,_____ nev - er,
don't for - get it. Love___ is their on - ly

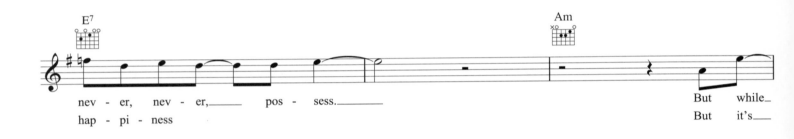

nev - er, nev - er,_____ pos - sess._____ But while___
hap - pi - ness But it's___

To Coda

___ she's there wait - ing,_____ and with-out them,___ try_____ a lit - tle
___ all so ea - sy_____ all you got to do is try_____ a lit - tle

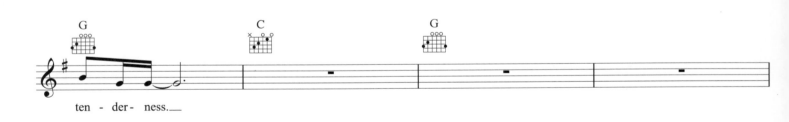

ten - der - ness.___

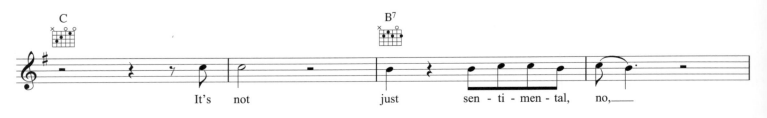

It's not just sen - ti - men - tal, no,___

she has   her grief   and care.___

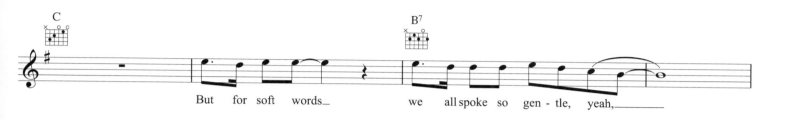

But for soft words___   we all spoke so gen - tle, yeah,_____

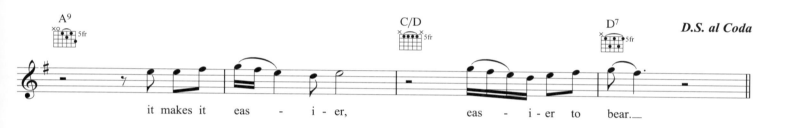

D.S. al Coda

it makes it   eas - i - er,   eas - i - er to bear.___

Coda

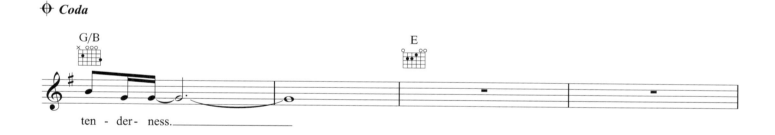

ten - der - ness._____

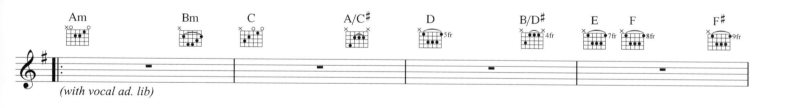

(with vocal ad. lib)

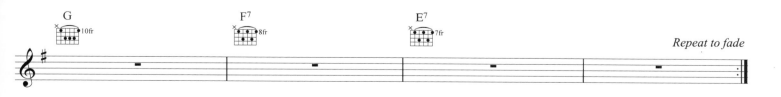

Repeat to fade

213

The Unforgiven
Words & Music by
James Hetfield, Lars Ulrich & Kirk Hammett

© Copyright 1991 Creeping Death Music, USA.
Universal Music Publishing Limited.
All rights in Germany administered by Universal Music Publ. GmbH.
All Rights Reserved. International Copyright Secured.

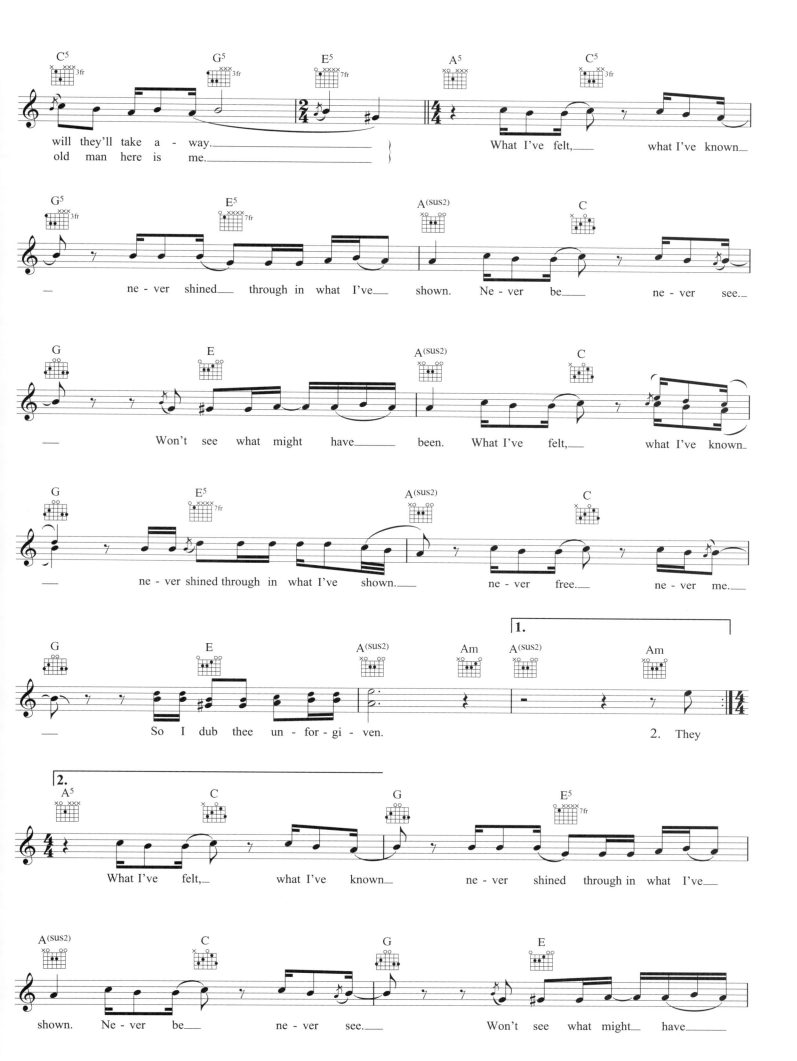

Use Somebody

Words & Music by
Caleb Followill, Nathan Followill, Jared Followill & Matthew Followill

© Copyright 2008 Followill Music/Martha Street Music/Songs Of Combustion (administered by Bug Music-Music Of Windswept) (55%)/
McFearless Music/Coffee Tea Or Me Publishing (adminstered by Bug Music Limited) (45%).
All Rights Reserved. International Copyright Secured.

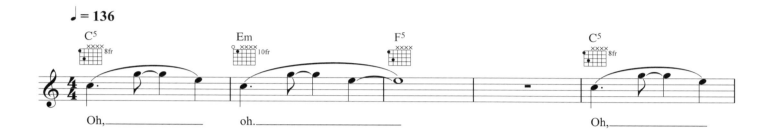

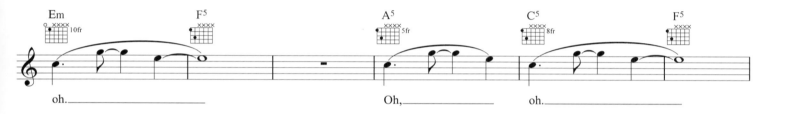

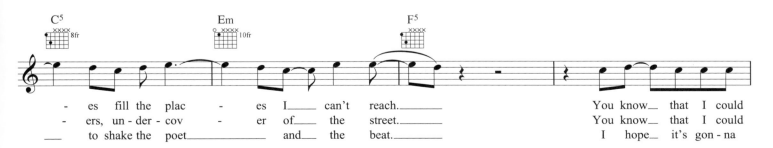

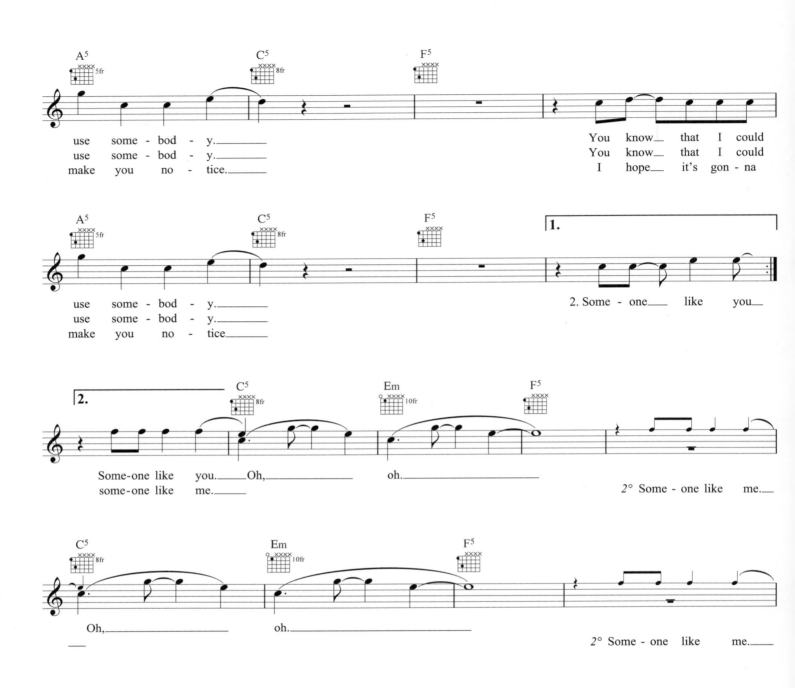

use some - bod - y._____
use some - bod - y._____
make you no - tice._____

You know__ that I could
You know__ that I could
I hope__ it's gon - na

use some - bod - y._____
use some - bod - y._____
make you no - tice_____

1.

2. Some - one__ like you__

2.

Some - one like you.__ Oh,_____ oh._____
some - one like me.____

2° Some - one like me.__

Oh,_____ oh.__
__

2° Some - one like me.__

Oh,_____ oh._____
__ Some - bod - y.

To Coda ⊕   *D.S. al Coda*

Oh,_____ oh.

3. Off in the night__

218

219

Up Around The Bend

Words & Music by John Fogerty

© Copyright 1970 Jondora Music, USA.
Prestige Music Limited.
By Permission Prestige Music Limited.
All Rights Reserved. International Copyright Secured.

4. Catch a ride___ to the end___ of the high - way,

and we'll meet___ by the big red tree.___ There's a place___ up a - head___

___ and I'm go - in'; come a - long,___ come a - long___ with___ me.___

Come on the ri - sing wind,___ we're go - in' up___ a - round the bend.___

Repeat and fade

Yeah! Do___ do do___ do, do___ do do___ do.

Viva La Vida

Words & Music by
Guy Berryman, Jon Buckland, Will Champion & Chris Martin

© Copyright 2008 Universal Music Publishing MGB Limited.
All rights in Germany administered by Musik Edition Discoton GmbH (a division of Universal Music Publishing Group).
All Rights Reserved. International Copyright Secured.

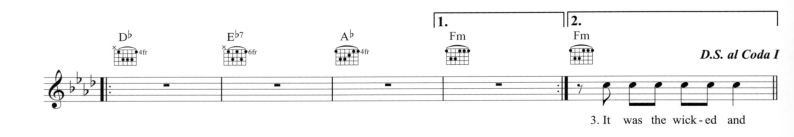

3. It was the wick-ed and

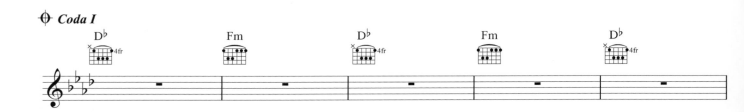

Coda I

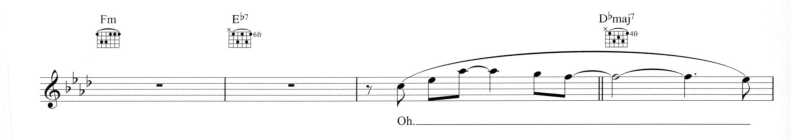

Oh.____

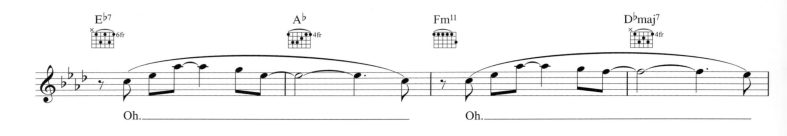

Oh.____   Oh.____

D.S.S. al Coda II

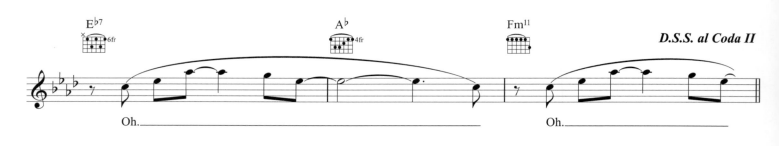

Oh.____   Oh.____

Coda II

Repeat and fade

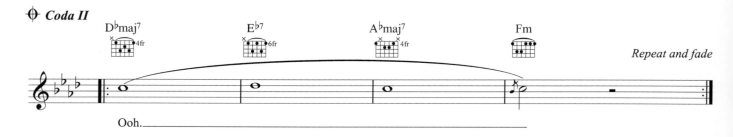

Ooh.____

Warwick Avenue

Words & Music by
Duffy, James Hogarth & Eg White

© Copyright 2006 EMI Music Publishing Limited (50%)/
Universal Music Publishing Limited (25%) (administered in Germany by Universal Music Publ. GmbH)/
Universal Music Publishing MGB Limited (25%) (administered in Germany by Musik Edition Discoton GmbH, a division of Universal Music Publishing Group).
All Rights Reserved. International Copyright Secured.

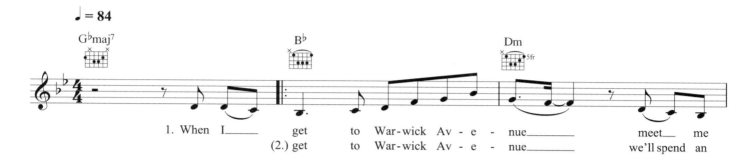

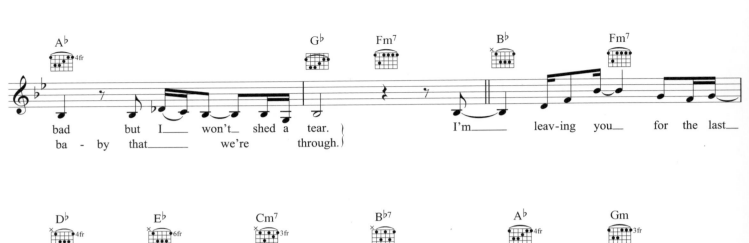

bad but I____ won't shed a tear. ⎫
ba - by that____ we're through. ⎭
I'm____ leav-ing you__ for the last__

__ time, ba - by. You think you're lov - ing_ but you don't love____ me.__ I've

_ been con - fused out of my__ mind late - ly. You think you're lov - ing_ but I

2° you

1.

want to be free. Ba - by you've hurt_ me.__

2.

2. When I____ don't love____ me.__ I want__ to__ be free. Ba - by,

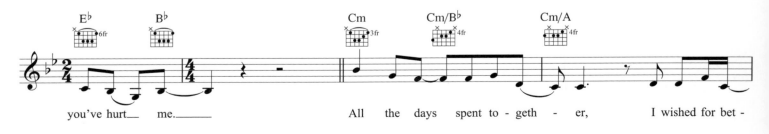

you've hurt_ me.__ All the days spent to - geth - er, I wished for bet -

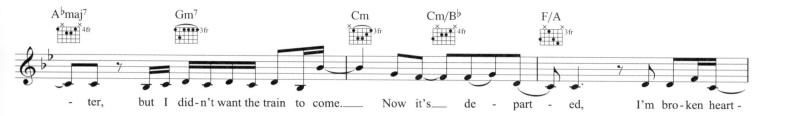

-ter, but I did-n't want the train to come.___ Now it's___ de-part-ed, I'm bro-ken heart-

-ed; seems like we nev-er start-ed. All those days___ spent to-geth - er, when I wished for bet-

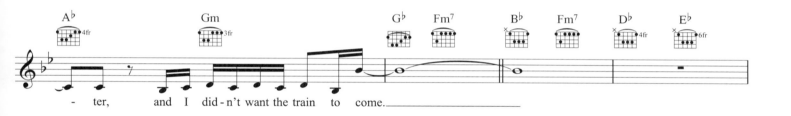

-ter, and I did-n't want the train to come._____

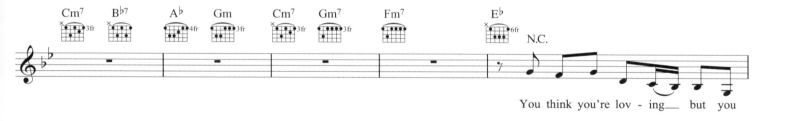

You think you're lov - ing___ but you

don't love___ me.___ I want___ to be free. Ba - by, you hurt___ me. You don't

___ love___ me.___ I want___ to be free. Ba - by, you've hurt___ me.

White Rabbit

Words & Music by Grace Slick

© Copyright 1967 Irving Music Incorporated/Copperpenny Music, USA.
Rondor Music (London) Limited.
All rights in Germany administered by Rondor Musikverlag GmbH.
All Rights Reserved. International Copyright Secured.

Wild Wood
Words & Music by Paul Weller

© Copyright 1993 Stylist Music Limited.
Universal Music Publishing MGB Limited.
All rights in Germany administered by Musik Edition Discoton GmbH (a division of Universal Music Publishing Group).
All Rights Reserved. International Copyright Secured.

With Or Without You

Words & Music by U2

© Copyright 1987 Blue Mountain Music Limited/Mother Music Limited/PolyGram International Music Publishing B.V.
All rights in Germany administered by Universal Music Publ. GmbH.
All Rights Reserved. International Copyright Secured.

232

Wonderful Tonight

Words & Music by Eric Clapton

© Copyright 1977, 1999 & 2004 Eric Clapton.
All Rights Reserved. International Copyright Secured.

1. It's late in the eve - ning, ___ she's wond-'ring what clothes
2. We go to a par - ty, ___ and ev - 'ry - one turns
3. It's time to go home ___ now, ___ and I've got an ach -

___ to wear. ___ She puts on her make ___ up, ___
___ to see ___ this beau - ti - ful la - dy ___
- ing head; ___ so I give her the car ___ keys, ___

and brush - es her long ___ blonde hair. ___ And then she asks
that's walk - ing a - round ___ with me. ___ And then she asks
and she helps me to bed. ___ And then I tell

___ me, "Do I look all ___ right?" ___ And I say,
___ me, "Do you feel all ___ right?" ___ And I say,
___ her as I turn out the light, ___ I say, "My

1.

To Coda ⊕

"Yes, you look won - der - ful ___ to - night." ___
"Yes, I feel won - der - ful ___ to - night." ___
dar - ling, you were won - der - ful ___ to - night."_

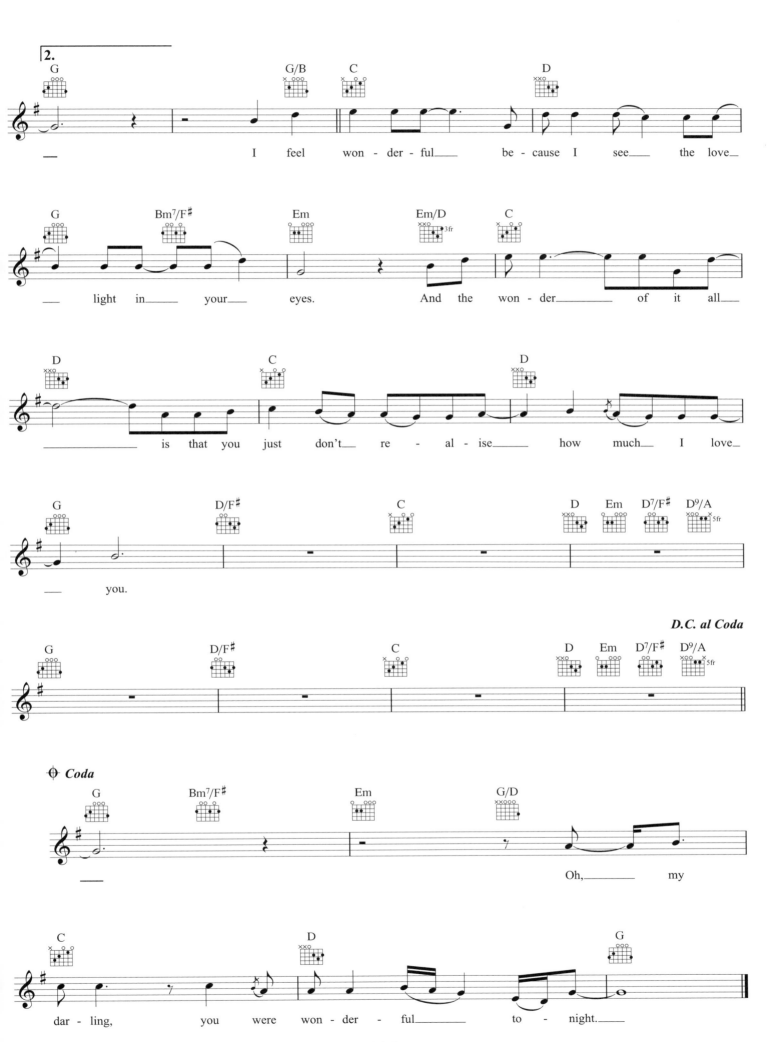

2.

I feel won-der-ful____ be-cause I see____ the love____

____ light in____ your____ eyes. And the won-der____ of it all____

_____ is that you just don't____ re - al - ise____ how much____ I love____

____ you.

D.C. al Coda

Coda

Oh,_____ my

dar-ling, you were won-der-ful to - night.____

235

Wonderful World, Beautiful People

Words & Music by Jimmy Cliff

© Copyright 1969 Island Music Limited.
Universal/Island Music Limited.
All rights in Germany administered by Universal Music Publ. GmbH.
All Rights Reserved. International Copyright Secured.

In - stead of fuss - ing and fight - ing, cheat - ing, back - fight - ing,

scand - al - i - sing and ha - ting. Ba - by, we___ could have a ___ ting. Yeah,___

___ we___ could have a won - der - ful world,_____ beau - ti - ful peo - ple,___

you and your girl,_____ things could be pret - ty,___ but un - der - neath___ this,

there is a sec - ret, that no - bod - y,___ can re - veal. *(Strings)*

Don't___ you know that won - der - ful world,_____

beau - ti - ful peo - ple,___ talk - ing 'bout you,___ talk - ing 'bout me,___

___ talk - ing 'bout Nix - on, Har - old Wil - son, Pom - pi - dou,___ it's the scene,___

Fade to end

___ ev - 'ry lit - tle bit helps___ now, do what you can. Ev - 'ry lit - tle bit helps___

237

You Can Get It If You Really Want

Words & Music by Jimmy Cliff

© Copyright 1970 Island Music Limited.
Universal/Island Music Limited.
All rights in Germany administered by Universal Music Publ. GmbH.
All Rights Reserved. International Copyright Secured.

239

You Never Can Tell

Words & Music by Chuck Berry

© Copyright 1964 Arc Music Corporation, USA.
Tristan Music Limited.
All Rights Reserved. International Copyright Secured.

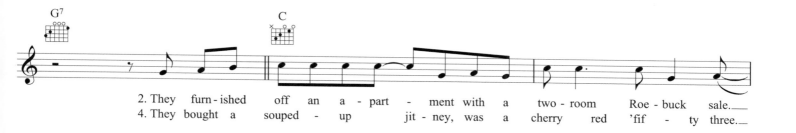

2. They furn-ished off an a-part - ment with a two-room Roe-buck sale.___
4. They bought a souped - up jit - ney, was a cherry red 'fif - ty three.___

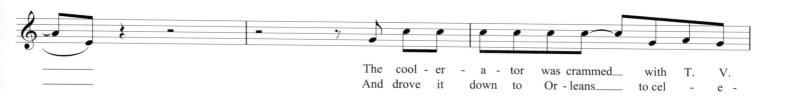

___ The cool - er - a - tor was crammed___ with T. V.
And drove it down to Or - leans___ to cel - e -

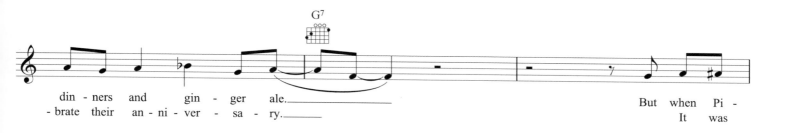

din - ners and gin - ger ale.___ But when Pi -
- brate their an - ni - ver - sa - ry.___ It was

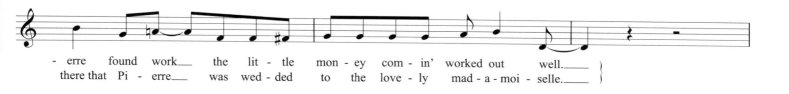

- erre found work___ the lit - tle mon - ey com - in' worked out well.___)
there that Pi - erre___ was wed - ded to the love - ly mad - a - moi - selle.___)

C'est la vie,___ say the old___ folks, it goes to show you nev - er can

1.   **2.**   *D.S. al Coda*   Coda

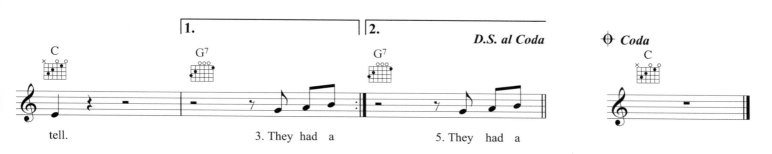

tell.   3. They had a   5. They had a

241

Your Latest Trick
Words & Music by Mark Knopfler

© Copyright 1985 Straitjacket Songs Limited.
Universal Music Publishing Limited.
All rights in Germany administered by Universal Music Publ. GmbH.
All Rights Reserved. International Copyright Secured.

1. All the
2. My
it's

late night bar - gains have been struck   be - tween the sat - in beaux and their belles,___
door was stand - ing___ o - pen,   se - cur - i - ty was laid - back and lax,___
past last call for al - co - hol,   past re - call has been here and gone.___

and pre - his - tor - ic gar - bage___ trucks___   have the
but it was on - ly my heart got bro - ken;___   you must have had
The land - lord fi - nal - ly paid us all;___   the sat - in

ci - ty to them - selves.___   Ech - oes roar, di -
a pass key made out of wax.   You played rob - ber - y with in - sol - ence and
jazz - men have put a - way their horns.___   And we're stand - ing out - side of this wond -

You've Got To Hide Your Love Away

Words & Music by
John Lennon & Paul McCartney

© Copyright 1965 Sony/ATV Music Publishing (UK) Limited.
All Rights Reserved. International Copyright Secured.

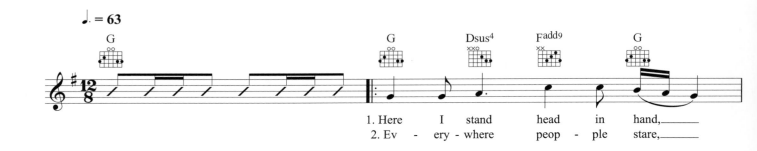

1. Here I stand head in hand,_____
2. Ev - ery - where peop - ple stare,_____

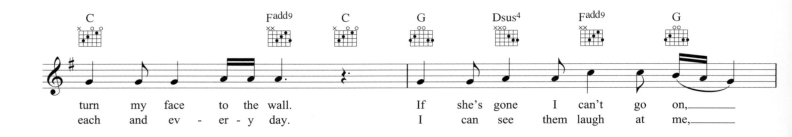

turn my face to the wall. If she's gone I can't go on,_____
each and ev - er - y day. I can see them laugh at me,_____

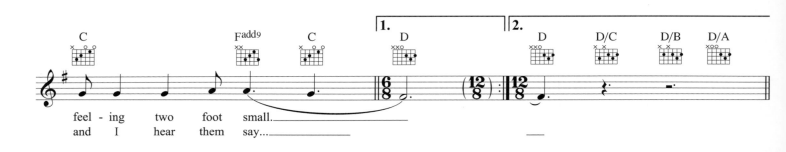

feel - ing two foot small._____
and I hear them say..._____

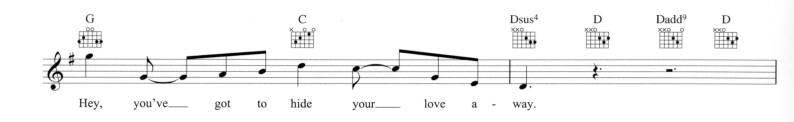

Hey, you've___ got to hide your___ love a - way.

Hey, you've___ got to hide your___ love a - way.

3. How can I even try,_____ I can never win,
4. How could she say to me,_____ love will find a way?

hear - ing them, see - ing them_____ in the state I'm in?_____
Gath - er round all you clowns,_____ let me hear you say..._____

1.

2.

Hey, you've got to hide your__ love a - way.

Hey, you've__ got to hide your_____ love a - way.

(Alto Flutes duet)

Wind Of Change

Words & Music by Klaus Meine

© Copyright 1990 PRI Music Incorporated, USA.
Universal Music Publishing Limited.
All rights in Germany administered by Universal Music Publ. GmbH.
All Rights Reserved. International Copyright Secured.

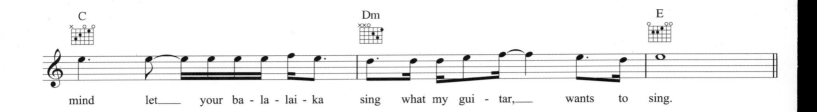
mind let__ your ba - la - lai - ka sing what my gui - tar,__ wants to sing.

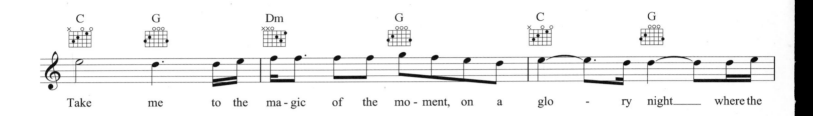
Take me to the ma - gic of the mo - ment, on a glo - ry night__ where the

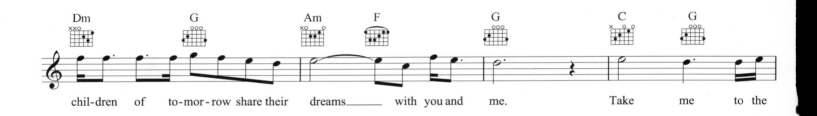
chil-dren of to-mor-row share their dreams__ with you and me. Take me to the

mag-ic of the mo-ment, on a glo - ry night__ where the chil-dren of to-mor-row dream a -

rall.   **a tempo**

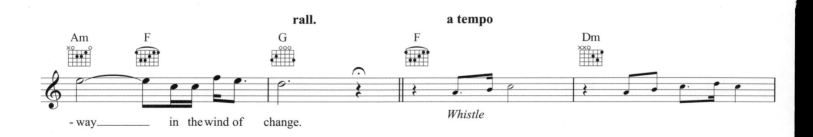
- way____ in the wind of change.   *Whistle*

rit.

23456789